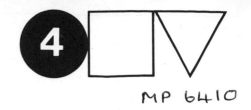

MP 6410

Computation and Structure 4

Nuffield Mathematics Project published for the Nuffield Foundation by W & R Chambers and John Murray

550 77005 4 (Chambers)
7195 1900 4 (Murray)

Manresa House.

Printed in Great Britain by
Newgate Press Limited
London EC1

General introduction

The aim of the Nuffield Mathematics Project is to devise a 'contemporary approach for children from 5 to 13'. The guides do not comprise an entirely new syllabus. The stress is on *how to learn*, not on what to teach. Running through all the work is the central notion that the children must be set free to make their own discoveries and think for themselves, and so achieve understanding, instead of learning off mysterious drills. In this way the whole attitude to the subject can be changed and 'Ugh, no, I didn't like maths' will be heard no more.

To achieve understanding young children cannot go straight to abstractions — they need to handle things ('apparatus' is too grand a word for at least some of the equipment concerned — conkers, beads, scales, globes, and so on).

But 'setting the children free' does not mean starting a riot with a roomful of junk for ammunition. The changeover to the new approach brings its own problems. The guide *I do, and I understand* (which is of a different character from the others) faces these problems and attempts to show how they can be overcome.

The other books fall into three categories: Teachers' Guides, Weaving Guides and Check-up Guides. The Teachers' Guides cover three main topics: ● Computation and Structure, ▼ Shape and Size, ■ Graphs Leading to Algebra. In the course of these guides the development of mathematics is seen as a spiral. The same concept is met over and over again and illustrated in a different way at every stage. The books do not cover years, or indeed any specific time; they simply develop themes and therefore show the teacher how to allow one child to progress at a different pace to another. They contain direct teaching suggestions, examples of apparently un-mathematical subjects and situations which can be used to develop a mathematical sense, examples of children's work, and suggestions for class discussions and out-of-school activities. The Weaving Guides are single-concept books which give detailed instructions or information about a particular subject.

The third category of books, as the name implies, will provide 'check-ups' on the children's progress. The traditional tests are difficult to administer in the new atmosphere of individual discovery and so our intention is to replace these by individual check-ups for individual children. These are being prepared by a team from the Institut des Sciences de l'Education in Geneva under the general supervision of Piaget. These check-ups, together with more general commentary, will be issued in the same format as the other guides and, in fact, be an integral part of the scheme.

While the books are a vital part of the Nuffield Mathematics Project, they should not be looked on as guides to the only 'right' way to teach mathematics. We feel very strongly that development from the work in the guides is more important than the guides themselves. They were written against the background of teachers' centres where ideas put forward in the books could be discussed, elaborated and modified. We hope very much that they will continue to be used in this way. A teacher by himself may find it difficult to use them without the reassurance and encouragement which come from discussion with others. Centres for discussion do already exist and we hope that many more will be set up.

The children's work that has been reproduced in these books, like the books themselves, is not supposed to be taken as a model of perfection. Some of it indeed contains errors. It should be looked upon as an example of work that children *might* produce rather than a model of work that they *should* produce.

Foreword

The last few years have been exciting ones for teachers of mathematics ; and for those of us who are amateurs in the subject but have a taste for it which was not wholly dulled by the old methods that are so often stigmatised, there has been abundant interest in seeing the new mathematical approach develop into one of the finest elements in the movement towards new curricula.

This is a crucial subject ; and, since a child's first years of work at it may powerfully affect his attitude to more advanced mathematics, the age range 5 to 13 is one which needs special attention. The Trustees of the Nuffield Foundation were glad in 1964 to build on the forward-looking ideas of many people and to set up the Nuffield Mathematics Project ; they were also fortunate to secure Dr. Geoffrey Matthews and other talented and imaginative teachers for the development team. The ideas of this team have helped in the growth of much lively activity, throughout the country, in new mathematical teaching for children : the Schools Council, the Local Education Authority pilot areas, and many individual teachers and administrators have made a vital contribution to this work, and the Trustees are very grateful for so much readiness to co-operate with the Foundation. The fruits of co-operation are in the books that follow ; and many a teacher will enter the classroom with a lively enthusiasm for trying out what is proposed in these pages.

Brian Young
Director of the Nuffield Foundation

Contents

Introduction

This Guide begins with decimals in connection with measurement, but formal development of fractions (involving operations) is deferred to the next volume, *Computation and Structure* ❺ . The bulk of the present Guide is devoted to the introduction of the integers, {. . . ⁻3, ⁻2, ⁻1, 0, ⁺1, ⁺2, ⁺3, . . .}. An attempt has been made to introduce these on a sound footing (so that the children can really understand, without being given 'tricks'), but within the 'primary' framework. As usual, what is **not** in the Guides is just as important as the development outlined here, that is, the spontaneous work of the children and the wide range of problems suggested by themselves. The Guide ends with an introduction to large numbers and indices, which children enjoy, for example, in connection with work on 'space'.

1 Extension of place value

Towards the end of *Computation and Structure* ❸, in the section headed 'Fractions', it was suggested that measurements of length should be carried out in tenths of an inch. The intention here was to introduce decimal fractions as soon as possible, because of their simplicity and as a natural extension of our system of place value.

It was pointed out that recording 27 tenths of an inch as 2·7 inches gave an idea of the real significance of the use of decimal fractions, not just a theoretical approach to the extension of 'H.T.U.' (Hundreds, Tens, Units).

Many teachers find this approach to linear measurement far more meaningful to children but, even so, it is perhaps as well now if some kind of consolidation of understanding is carried out by using the abacus again, this time adapting it so that there are two places to the right of the units column, e.g.

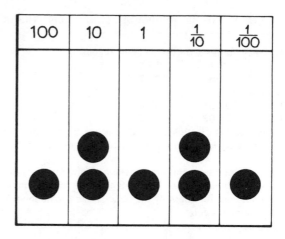

A 'counting-board' with counters

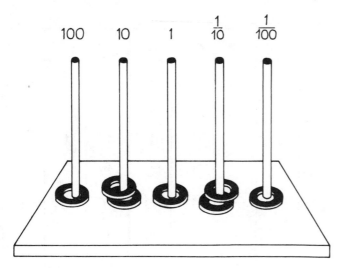

A 'decimal' abacus with washers

It should be noted that we are not yet advocating any operations with decimal fractions. We are still confining them to practical purposes, using the abacus for an understanding of the extension of place value. Results only are written down or recorded, i.e. children can put washers on the appropriate columns and then record the result of this.

Simple exercises like the following could be carried out:

Record these numbers on the decimal abacus:

3·2   5·1   10·5
101·6   5·9   425·7

Now do these:

101·11   101·01   58·03
68·13   78·02   100·08

Recording numbers in this way, what is the highest number of washers or counters which would occur in any one column?

Using only 3 counters each time, make as many numbers as you can on your decimal abacus. Use all 3 counters for each number. Make 20 different numbers (if the abacus has 4 columns). Two have been done for you.

Write out the numbers in order of size, putting the smallest first.

Record the following as decimal fractions. A ruler with tenths may help you if you are not sure.
Examples:

Examples $4\frac{1}{2} = 4\cdot5$, $6\frac{7}{10} = 6\cdot7$

$\frac{4}{10}$, $1\frac{1}{10}$, $2\frac{3}{10}$, $3\frac{6}{10}$

$4\frac{8}{10}$, $5\frac{9}{10}$, $6\frac{10}{10}$, $20\frac{1}{2}$

$12\frac{4}{10}$, $7\frac{5}{10}$, $5\frac{4}{10}$, $8\frac{2}{10}$

Children can be helped towards an understanding of the decimal form of recording by using bicimals when measuring. This is easier and requires only the symbols 0 and 1.

e.g.

$\frac{1}{2}$ inch may be recorded as	·1 inch (bicimal)
$\frac{1}{4}$ inch as	·01 inch (bicimal)
$\frac{3}{4}$ inch as	·11 inch (bicimal)
$1\frac{1}{2}$ inches as	1·1 inch (bicimal)

$9\frac{3}{4}$ inches would be recorded later as 1001·11 inches. (It must be recalled that all measurement is approximate. '$9\frac{3}{4}$ inches' would be an **estimate** of an actual length.) Children familiar with the binary scale should have no trouble with this form of recording. Its particular value is the obvious 'practical' difference between, say, lengths whose bicimal representations are 1·1 and 1·01 and 1·001 inches.

Class discussion could be a means of constructing a table, perhaps on a blackboard, in order to build up the idea of measuring and recording in bicimals, e.g.

Bicimal recording

	8 in	4in	2 in	1in	$\frac{1}{2}$ in	$\frac{1}{4}$ in	$\frac{1}{8}$ in
$1\frac{1}{2}$ in				1	1		
$1\frac{1}{4}$ in				1	0	1	
$1\frac{3}{4}$ in				1	1	1	
$2\frac{1}{2}$ in			1	0	1		
$2\frac{1}{8}$ in			1	0	0	0	1
$4\frac{1}{2}$ in		1	0	0	1		
$5\frac{1}{4}$ in		1	0	1	0	1	
$7\frac{3}{4}$ in		1	1	1	1	1	
$9\frac{3}{8}$ in	1	0	0	1	0	1	1
$10\frac{1}{2}$ in	1	0	1	0	1		

Decimal Abacus — Andrew Parnley

We made a decimal abacus using a block piece of polystyrene and pipe cleaners inside straws. We made our own washers from cardboard.

Then we recorded the following numbers on the abacus.

3·2

5·1

10·5

101·6

5·9

25·7

101·11

101·01

58·03

68·13

78·02

100·08

Bicimal Recordings.

Objects Measured	measurement in inches.	Bicimals
Diameter of Flower pot	5 ½ ins	101·1
Height of milk bottle.	5 ½ ins	101·1
Length of Pencil.	5 ½ ins	101·1
Length of Lynn's foot.	8 ½ ins	1000·1
Height of Flower pot.	8 ½ ins	1000·1
Length of Debra's hair.	14 ½ ins	1110·1
Width of Window.	23 ins	10111·0
Width of Mrs Selbys desk.	24 ins	11000·0
Length of Desk.	38 ins	100110·0
		by K. Durie

Assignments could then take the form of measuring the usual classroom objects that are familiar to children:

Exercise book
Desk top
Pencil
Reading book
Window ledges, etc.

and the recording completed in bicimals, e.g.
My pencil is approximately 110·11 inches long (bicimal).

More difficult measuring exercises could follow, e.g.

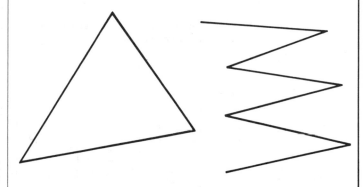

Measure some round things (how?) and record in bicimals, e.g. tin lids.

Now measure the perimeter of other shapes and record in the same way. Start by measuring these:

Find some shapes of your own and record the measurements of their perimeters using bicimals.

Questions requiring order of size can follow, e.g.

These are bicimal recordings of some measurements in inches:

101·01	110·11	111·111	1·001
1·011	111·011	110·111	

Which is the longest?
Which is the shortest?

Put them in order of size starting with the longest.

Weighing assignments using the binary scale can also be used with added effect at this stage. Reference to pp. 29, 30 of *Computation and Structure* ❷ will recall weighing experiences when the children are asked to record the weights of parcels in terms of the actual weights used, e.g.

	1lb	8oz	4oz	2oz	1oz
Parcel A (2oz)				1	0
Parcel B (4oz)			1	0	0
Parcel D (12oz)	1	1	0	0	

The $\frac{1}{2}$ oz and $\frac{1}{4}$ oz weights could now be introduced and the above extended to binary fractions of an ounce, as in length, e.g.

2lb 4$\frac{1}{2}$oz would be recorded as 100100·1oz

Results can also be expressed in lb:

2lb 4oz would be recorded as 10·01 lb

From recording measurement and weight in the scale of 2, and through appropriate discussion and experiences, children will now be able to appreciate decimal recording more clearly. They will no doubt have had the suggested experiences of measuring in tenths of an inch, recording these in decimal notation, e.g.

2 $\frac{8}{10}$ inches as 2·8 inches

Recording measurements in hundredths is not very practicable with feet and inches, but the metric system provides us with this opportunity. This seems to be a natural follow-on from recording in bicimals and decimals, giving many opportunities for a meaningful use of the latter.

Whilst there is no need for an elaborate study of the metric system of weights and measures, it does seem advisable and topical that our upper Juniors should have some awareness of and familiarity with units such as the metre, kilometre, centimetre, kilogram, gram and litre. The ease of, say, converting 17 kilometres to metres can be compared with the conversion of 17 miles to yards (which is not advocated as a reasonable exercise). Tins and packets of commercial products can now be found with weights given in the metric system and a small collection of these could be the basis of group or class discussion.

Measuring length in the metric system could arise from something like the following:

Find the metre rule and look closely at how it is sub-divided.

You should observe that a metre is divided into 10 decimetres and each decimetre into 10 centimetres.

Obtain a school ruler which has these measurements. You should also notice that a centimetre is divided into 10 millimetres.

Which scale or base are we working in?
What else do you work with in this scale?

Make a ruler of your own from a piece of card or paper, 1 decimetre long. Now mark on the centimetres.

Using your own decimetre ruler, measure a few things like your exercise book, pencil, desk top, reading book, parts of your body, and record these measurements. You will find it impossible to be exact about this. What is the best you can do? Does 'work to the nearest centimetre' help you? Discuss with your teacher what you understand by this.

If one of the measurements you make is about 1 decimetre long, how would you record this as part of a metre?

How would you record 1 centimetre as part of a metre?

See if the following table will help you:

measurement	metres	dm	cm
1 metre 2 dm	1	2	
5 metres 3 dm 1 cm	5	3	1
8 decimetres		8	
6 centimetres		0	6
4 metres 3 dm			
8 metres 6 cm			
3 metres 5 dm			
2 metres 8 cm			
8 dm 4 cm			

Can you complete this table?

The Metre Rule

The metre rule is divided into ten equal parts
called decimetres. Each decimetre is divided
into ten equal parts called centimetres. On my
own school ruler I find that a centimetre is
divided into ten equal parts called millimetres.
If we use the decimal system 6m 4 dm can be
written as 6·4 metres.

From the Ruler	In Decimals
5m 3 dm →	5·3m
7dm 2 cm →	·72m
35 cm →	·35m
12 dm →	1·2m
4m 3dm 2mm →	4·302m
2dm 6cm 7mm →	·267m
5m 0dm 3cm →	5·03m

Practical work using the metre rule can follow and though the initial recording of measurements may be of the 'full form', e.g. 2 metres 3 dm 6 cm, children should be encouraged as soon as possible to record in metres and decimal fractions of a metre, e.g.

2 metres 3dm 6cm as 2·36 metres
or 23·6dm
or 236cm

Make some measurements with the metre rule and record to the nearest decimetre. When you have measured and recorded six things, discuss your accuracy with your teacher. For instance, was it a good idea to work to the nearest decimetre? Why not? What would have been better? Measure and record again.

Compare the metre rule with the English yard ruler.

Which is the longer?

Record the difference in length, as near as you are able to say. In inches you could record the difference like this:
3·3 < Difference < 3·4 (in inches)
meaning that you recognise the difference as being **more than** (perhaps only slightly) 3·3 inches but **less than** 3·4 inches.

Can you now record the difference in centimetres in this way?

. . . < Difference < . . . (in centimetres)

You have previously been recording six and three tenths inches as 6·3 inches. How would three metres and six tenths of a metre be recorded?
Users of the metric system would not write 3dm 4cm; they would record this measurement as 3·4dm or 34cm. How do you think they would record the following:
6 metres 4dm
5 metres 3dm
7 decimetres 2cm
35 centimetres
12 decimetres
4 metres 3dm 2cm
2dm 6cm 7mm
5 metres 0dm 3cm

Do you think this system of recording in decimals is easier than the one you are used to? Why?

It may be of some use to compare the English measures with those of the metric system. If metric measuring equipment is available children might be asked to find out things for themselves.

Find out which of our English measures is nearest to the following metric measures, e.g.
                    Nearest English measure
1 kilometre   1 mile
1 metre
1 litre

Can you find out and complete the following rough comparisons for English and metric measures?

. . . cm   > 1 inch   > . . . cm
. . . litres > 1 gallon   > . . . litres
. . . lb   > 1 kilogram > . . . lb

Discuss your recordings with your teacher.

What measures do you think a person on the continent would use to measure the following:
The distance of a car journey
The weight of fruit and vegetables
The volume of petrol or any liquids
The weight of packets of tobacco
Lengths of cloth for dress-making
The lengths of the sides of pencil-drawn shapes in an exercise book
The weight of sacks of coal

In connection with car travel, many children will have heard references to kilometres, especially as so many people go to the continent for holidays. They may be slightly familiar with foreign currency. Litres they may have heard of in connection with the capacity of car engines or quantities of petrol; kilograms and grams they may have met when shopping. Comparisons between our measures and metric ones can be useful, and 'ready-reckoner' graphs could be made to illustrate these. Children like these if only for the apparent 'magic' of easy conversions. Certainly they are preferable to multiplication by $\frac{8}{5}$ or $\frac{5}{8}$: this seems to do nothing but confuse children of primary-school age, which is confirmation again of the fact that operations with vulgar or decimal fractions are best left alone at our present stage.

Another useful aid for illustrating the scale of 10, and recording in tenths, is the surveyor's chain.

A chain is 66 ft (i.e. 22 yd) long and it is divided up into 100 links. A brass tablet marks every tenth link. The shape of the tablet shows the distance from the nearer end of the chain.

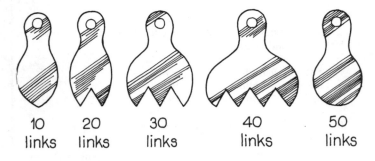

| 10 links | 20 links | 30 links | 40 links | 50 links |

This apparatus can provide a useful exercise for children in measuring longer distances and recording their measurements in chains and tenths or hundredths of a chain, e.g.
4 chains 30 links could be recorded as 4·3 chains.
4 chains 34 links could be recorded as 4·34 chains, and so on.

The Dienes M.A.B. apparatus is also a handy set of material for measuring and recording in the metric system.

Measure the edges of a unit cube in the set of Dienes apparatus. Use centimetres.

Now measure
a long
a flat
a block

Record your measurements
a **in centimetres**
b **as decimal parts of a metre**

The pendulum can be a useful topic for experiment and discussion.

Make a simple pendulum (some string and a ball of Plasticine) and find the time taken for one half swing of this pendulum. A 'half swing' is from one end of the path across to the other, so that 'there and back' is a full swing. Start with a string length of 1½ metres. Shorten the length by 10cm each time. (Time, say, 20 half swings and find from this the time taken for one half swing.)

Draw a graph of your findings.

Try to find the length of string needed for a '1-second pendulum' (i.e. 1 second for 1 half swing).

How accurate do you think your result is?

Bulbs and corms are often sold according to their circumference. e.g.

Top Size	**12cm and above**
Size A	**10cm and up to 12cm**
Size B	**8cm and up to 10cm**
Size C	**Below 8cm**

We could record the above as:

Top Size	**12cm ≤ Circumference**
Size A	**10cm ≤ Circumference < 12cm**
Size B	**8cm ≤ Circumference < 10cm**
Size C	**Circumference < 8cm**

[**NB** The symbol ≤ means **'less than or equal to'**. Thus Top Size bulbs have a circumference more than or equal to 12cm.]

Obtain about 30 bulbs or corms (or conkers). Decide on the measurements of sub-sets into which they are to be sorted and record these as in the example. Can you adjust the measurements for the sub-sets so that the numbers in each are approximately equal?

From varied experiences in recording decimal fractions and using the metric system children should gain a meaningful awareness of the practical use of the extension to our decimal system of notation. It has also been an intention here to build up an awareness of upper and lower limits when measuring. Children are often confused when they do not seem to be able to get things exactly right. This is understandable, especially when they land at an 'in between' mark, e.g. somewhere between 6 and 7 tenths. We must encourage them to be as accurate as the tools and materials they are using will allow, but to be aware of the limits to which they are working.

Experiences and practice as follows may help:

> Put these numbers in order of size, the smallest first:
> a **11·1**   **11·0**   **111·0**   **1·1**   (bicimals)
> b **10·1**   **1·01**   **101**   **0·10** (bicimals)
> c   **6·7**   **67**   **7·6**   **6·07**
> d   **1·23**   **123·0**   **12·3**   **3·12**

> Write a number with a decimal fraction:
> 1 **between 3 and 4**
> 2 **between 8 and 9**
> 3 **just bigger than 5**
> 4 **between 6 and 6½**
> 5 **between ½ and ·7**
> 6 **just smaller than 9**

> If we were measuring the edge of a 1-inch cube with a ruler marked in centimetres and millimetres we should find that our measurement comes between 2·5cm and 2·6cm. So we could record as:
> **2·5 < length < 2·6 (in centimetres)**
>
> If our ruler could possibly have the millimetres divided up into 10 parts we could then record even more accurately:
> **2·53 < length < 2·55 (in centimetres)**
>
> But this is dependent on how well we can see these tiny divisions on the scale, how accurately the cube has been made, and whether the ruler is held in the right position. Draw a line 1 inch long (as accurately as possible) and then measure it in centimetres recording the limits between which your measurement lies.
>
> What could you say about the age of someone in your class who is '10 years old'?

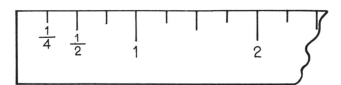

Children will not always want to record in this way using inequalities, e.g. for the length shown as 1¼ < length in inches < 1½. Instead, working to the nearest ¼ inch, they could write '1½ inches'. This would mean 'nearer to 1½ than to

1¼ or 1¾' (actually this implies 1⅜ inches < length < 1⅝ inches). The degree of accuracy (e.g. 'to the nearest inch' or 'to the nearest ⅛ of an inch') should be specified if this method of recording is used.

Nearly all children will have seen the speedometer on a car and the mileage recorder. This can be a useful aid to recording in tenths.

> The mileage recorder for a car looks like this:
>
>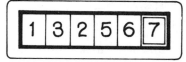
>
> The distance is given in miles and tenths of a mile. The right-hand digit (which may be in red) shows tenths of a mile.
>
> The columns of the recorder go like this:
>
> | 10,000 | 1,000 | 100 | 10 | 1 | tenths |
> |--------|-------|-----|----|---|--------|
> | 1 | 3 | 2 | 5 | 6 | 7 |
>
> The number on this mileage recorder is: thirteen thousand two hundred and fifty-six, and seven tenths.
>
> Write down these mileages in words:
> 24290·3
>   136·7
> 6570·5
> 1999·9
> 1000·0
> 411·7
>
> What will be the next number to show on the indicator if it now reads:
> 1234·5   1000·0   999·9
> 5326·9   6819·3   584·6

Problems of the following kind could be discussed and tried.

> At sea-level the air pressure is said to be approximately 14·5lb on every square inch. How much less than 15lb is this? How much more than 14lb is this? Record this weight in two different ways (using > for one and < for the other), both showing that it is more than 14lb but less than 15lb.

Other useful topics which can help illuminate the use of decimal fractions are:
Body temperatures
Recorded times of athletes
Barometer readings

The children should provide their own figures, e.g.
let them take their own temperatures, time their own performances, read the barometer, etc.

These can also be useful for discussing the degree of accuracy of the particular measuring instruments — and the degree of accuracy of recorded figures.

Useful number work can be along these lines:

Count up in steps of 0·1 from zero to 1·1 and write down each number you come to.

What is the value of the 4 in each of these numbers:
204·3
343·2
110·4
126·04
4286·01

Where would you put the decimal point if each 3 in the following numbers denotes 3 tens?
4312   3689
41300   23456

The 8 in the following numbers should mean 8 tenths. Put the decimal point in to make this true.
3718   5684   28

Write down the bigger one of each of the following pairs of numbers:
1·5   1·6
7·04   7·40
8·10   8·01
3·2   3·19

Now use this sign > to show your choice.

2 Modular arithmetic

Until now we have been concerned only with the set of numbers {0, 1, 2, 3, 4, . . .} but it is becoming clear that we need other numbers to proceed with further mathematics. Teachers will readily see the need for 'positive and negative integers' {. . . ⁻3, ⁻2, ⁻1, 0, ⁺1, ⁺2, ⁺3, . . .}. An example of this need is contained in the simple illustration $4 - 5 = \square$.

The operations of subtraction and division have been delayed deliberately until the appropriate sets of numbers have been constructed. It has already been mentioned that '3 from 2 I can't' is a possible barrier to the acceptance of integers at a later stage. Offering the physical process of 'taking away' as the complete analogue for subtraction is another possible reason for confusion when the mathematical operation of subtraction is encountered with integers (and later, vectors and matrices). The desire to reduce operations to a mechanical technique is also partially responsible for a lack of understanding. Sooner or later the 'trick' does not seem to work any more. Nowhere is this more evident than in the operations of subtraction and division.

We can help the understanding of these operations, by at least giving children the opportunity to see what is required, by using miniature arithmetic systems, sometimes called clock, remainder, or modular arithmetic. Although we are advocating the use of modular arithmetic mainly for an understanding of the operations and their requirements, teachers can also feel that it helps give practice with numbers, even to the extent of helping with 'tables' and 'what's left' when dealing with weights and measures. This, however, is certainly not meant to be the primary justification for using it. In *Computation and Structure* ❷ (page 86) we introduced modular arithmetic by using the clock and then constructing an addition table for mod 12.

Mod 12 from our method of reckoning time on the 12-hour clock is an obvious choice for a starting-point, and most children will also have become familiar with the addition table for the families of **odd** and **even** numbers when O and E are used to represent the families (see *Computation and*

Structure ❷ , page 78) and also with the table for arithmetic mod 2 (*Computation and Structure* ❷ , page 90).

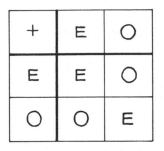

By discussion, or children's own discoveries, using 'tables' like the above and posing problems as below it will be found that 'answers' can be obtained to every problem in addition and subtraction, e.g.

$$E + \square = O \qquad O + \square = O$$
$$O + \square = O \qquad \square + O = 1$$
$$O + O = \square \qquad 1 + \square = O$$
$$E + E = \square \qquad 1 + \square = 1$$

The important properties of commutativity and associativity can be appreciated from these 'models' for a particular operation, in this case addition.
e.g.
Is $E + O = O + E$?
or
$0 + 1 = 1 + 0$?
Is $E + (O + O) = (E + O) + O$?
or
$(0 + 1) + 1 = 0 + (1 + 1)$?

Some other useful work can be obtained from a many-to-one mapping which illustrates the correspondence of each of the natural numbers (with zero) to the remainder it leaves after division by a certain number, say 4. We do not actually need to divide to produce the correspondence if we first of all set out the correspondence as:

Mod 4

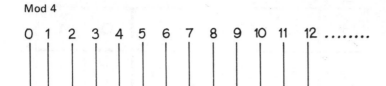

The many-to-one mapping can be displayed as below:

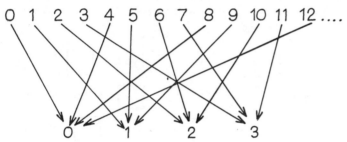

This illustrates the fact that in modular arithmetic we are dealing with 'equivalence classes' of natural numbers. In arithmetic modulo 4 two natural numbers are 'equivalent', and are in the same equivalence class, if they leave the same remainder on division by 4; so there are four equivalence classes: 0, 4, 8, ... ; 1, 5, 9, ... ; 2, 6, 10, ... and 3, 7, 11, ... All the members of the first class, for example, are mapped on to 0 in the diagram above.

On a mod 4 'clock' the same position is reached after 2, 6, 10, ... quarter turns from 0, and the position labelled 2 could instead be labelled 6, or 10, etc. Similarly, the 0 position could be labelled 4, or 8, etc.

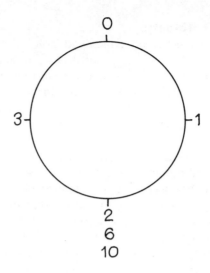

In fact, labels such as 4, 5, 6, 7, or even 8, 5, 2, 11, could be used instead of 0, 1, 2, 3 since these sets of four numbers contain one number from each equivalence class. The labels 4, 8, 2, 3, however, would not serve the purpose, for although 4, 2, 3 would label three of the positions, 8 would not serve to label the remaining one because it belongs to the same class as 4.

On a calendar, the same day of the week is reached after 1, 8, 15, 22 days. Another day is achieved after 3, 10, 17, 24 days. A mod 7 'clock' could be used to illustrate this. The finite set of numbers 0, 1, 2, 3, 4, 5, 6 could be used (or the set 7, 8, 9, 10, 11, 12, 13, or 14, 1, 2, 10, 11, 5, 6) or the days of the week, e.g.

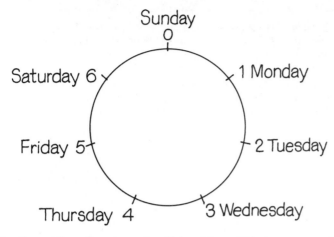

Sunday 0

Monday 1

Tuesday 2

Wednesday 3

Thursday 4

Friday 5

Saturday 6

count on first 3 positions and then count on 5 positions further, and observe that the final position could have been reached by simply counting on 1 position from the original one, $3 + 5 = 1$. This second method (with which it is not necessary for the markings on the 'clock' to be labelled at all) though less familiar than the first, is to be preferred, for in the second method, **all** the numbers are represented in the same way, by counting on; and because of this it is easier to see that addition is commutative and associative.

Starting at 0 or Sunday, after 7 (or 14, or 21) days, we arrive back at 0.

It is important to notice that addition in modular arithmetic with any modulus is both commutative and associative.

Thus
$3 + 5 = 1 = 5 + 3$ (mod 7)
$(4 + 6) + 2 = 3 + 2 = 5$ (mod 7)
and
$4 + (6 + 2) = 4 + 1 = 5$ (mod 7)

Because addition has these properties, successive additions can be carried out in any order, and brackets are unnecessary.

Thus
$4 + 5 + 6$ (mod 7)
can be evaluated as
$(4 + 5) + 6 = 2 + 6 = 1$
or as
$4 + (5 + 6) = 4 + 4 = 1$
or as
$(4 + 6) + 5 = 3 + 5 = 1$, or in many other ways.

These facts can be illustrated from a table for addition mod 7, or by using a mod 7 'clock'. An addition, such as $3 + 5$, can be illustrated on the 'clock' in two ways. In the first way, we begin at position 3, and count on clockwise 5 positions to end at position 1. In the second way, we begin at **any** position,

Pretend that we have only the numbers 0, 1 and 2, and make a 'clock' to help you do some 'arithmetic' in this system. The dial can be made from a piece of thin card, and the hand or pointer from a pipe cleaner, e.g.

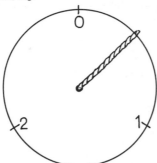

The pipe cleaner is pushed through the centre of the dial. The two ends are then pulled together and twisted. To find what $1 + 2$ is in this system, set the pointer to 1, and then move it clockwise 2 positions from 1 : we arrive at 0, and write $1 + 2 = 0$. Working in this way, complete the following addition table for this 'arithmetic modulo 3':

+ mod 3	O	1	2
O			
1			O
2			

Compare the values of $1 + 2$ and $2 + 1$; of $0 + 1$ and $1 + 0$; and of $0 + 2$ and $2 + 0$. Is addition commutative in this arithmetic?

Compare also the values of $(1 + 1) + 2$ and $1 + (1 + 2)$; of $(1 + 0) + 2$ and $1 + (0 + 2)$; and of $(2 + 1) + 2$ and $2 + (1 + 2)$. Is addition associative in this arithmetic?

$1 + 2 = 0$ can also be illustrated on the 'clock' in another way. Set the pointer at **any** position, move it on 1 position, and then 2 further positions, and notice that its final position is the same as that at which it started. How would you use this method to show that $2 + 2 = 1$ and $1 + 1 = 2$ in this arithmetic?

Work similar to that suggested in the last card should be carried out with several different moduli, perhaps using times in hours with a mod 12 'clock', and days of the week with a mod 7 one. From this work, children should learn to add in modular arithmetic, and appreciate that addition is both commutative and associative, and that 0 is a 'neutral' element for addition because the result of adding 0 to any number is to leave it unaltered.

Our main purpose here is to use modular arithmetic as an introduction to the integers, particularly with reference to the operation of subtraction. Its relevance for this purpose was discussed briefly in *Computation and Structure* **3** and we return to the subject now in more detail. The next page is for the teacher only at this stage.

In any situation where addition is defined, to subtract **b** from **a** is to find what must be added to **b** to give **a**. It is clear from this definition that subtraction is an awkward, indirect procedure, but when we are working in the set {0, 1, 2, 3, . . .} nothing can be done to simplify it; and, furthermore, sometimes the operation cannot be carried out at all in this set: for example, we cannot subtract 3 from 2. But when the system of integers {. . . −2, −1, 0, +1, +2, . . .} has been introduced, the indirect procedure of subtraction can be replaced by a **direct** procedure, that of addition of another number, called the 'additive inverse' (see below), and this addition can always be carried out. Now in modular arithmetic, too, subtraction can be replaced by addition of the 'additive inverse', and this addition can always be carried out; so that modular arithmetic provides a very good introduction to one of the properties of the integers, and it is developed here for that purpose.

In modular arithmetic, corresponding to every number there is a second number, called its **additive inverse**, such that the sum of the two numbers is 0.

To see this in the familiar mod 12 (clock) arithmetic, consider the following addition table:

Mod 12

+	0	1	2	3	4	5	6	7	8	9	10	11
0	0	1	2	3	4	5	6	7	8	9	10	11
1	1	2	3	4	5	6	7	8	9	10	11	0
2	2	3	4	5	6	7	8	9	10	11	0	1
3	3	4	5	6	7	8	9	10	11	0	1	2
4	4	5	6	7	8	9	10	11	0	1	2	3
5	5	6	7	8	9	10	11	0	1	2	3	4
6	6	7	8	9	10	11	0	1	2	3	4	5
7	7	8	9	10	11	0	1	2	3	4	5	6
8	8	9	10	11	0	1	2	3	4	5	6	7
9	9	10	11	0	1	2	3	4	5	6	7	8
10	10	11	0	1	2	3	4	5	6	7	8	9
11	11	0	1	2	3	4	5	6	7	8	9	10

To add two of these numbers, we add normally, except that every time we reach 12 we say 0 and start again. Thus:

$3 + 4 = 7$
$3 + 8 = 11$
$3 + 9 = 0$
$3 + 10 = 1$
$8 + 4 = 0$
$9 + 8 = 5$
etc.

Eight hours after 9 o'clock is 5 o'clock; 7 hours after 6 o'clock is 1 o'clock, and so on.

In this system, every number does have an additive inverse. That is, whatever number we start with, we can find a number which, when added to the first one, gives 0 (or 12, or 24, or whatever number we are using from the set 0, 12, 24, 36, . . .). For example, the additive inverse of 9 is 3 because $9 + 3 = 0$; the additive inverse of 8 is 4 because $8 + 4 = 0$, and so on.

The complete table of additive inverses is:

Number	Additive inverse
0	0
1	11
2	10
3	9
4	8
5	7
6	6
7	5
8	4
9	3
10	2
11	1

Now $5 - 8 = 9$, because, as we see from the addition table, 9 is the number which, when added to 8, gives 5: $8 + \boxed{9} = 5$. Now the additive inverse of 8 is 4 (because $8 + 4 = 0$); and $5 + 4 = 9$, i.e. **$5 - 8 = 5 +$ (additive inverse of 8)**. This is an example of the general result that subtracting a number gives the same result as adding its 'additive inverse' (see Appendix).

Notice that subtraction in modular arithmetic, unlike addition, is neither commutative nor associative. Thus $3 - 5 = 10$ (mod 12), whilst $5 - 3 = 2$ (mod 12); and $5 - (4 - 2) = 3$ (mod 12), whilst $(5 - 4) - 2 = 11$ (mod 12).

To provide interesting work for children, the foregoing explanations for teachers must of course be simplified.

Using the addition table for arithmetic modulo 3 that you made earlier, find what you add to 2, in this arithmetic, to give 0. What do you add to 1 to give 0? What do you add to 2 to give 1? $1 - 2$ means the number which must be added to 2 to give 1: so that $1 - 2 = \square$ means the same as $2 + \square = 1$. What is the value of $1 - 2$? i.e. what number must be written in the box to make $1 - 2 = \square$ a true statement? Finding the value of $1 - 2$ is called 'subtracting 2 from 1'.

What are the values of $2 - 1, 1 - 0, 0 - 1, 0 - 2$?

Make up a subtraction table like the addition table for this arithmetic. Is there an answer to every subtraction sum? Can you find any subtraction which cannot be carried out in this arithmetic?

Can every subtraction be carried out in the arithmetic of the ordinary numbers 0, 1, 2, 3, 4, . . . ?

Compare the values of $2 - 1$ and $1 - 2$ in arithmetic mod 3, and also the values of $(2 - 0) - 1$ and $2 - (0 - 1)$. What can you say about the operation of subtraction? Can you think of anything you can say about addition that you cannot say about subtraction?

Work similar to that suggested in the last card should be carried out with several different moduli, for example, 4, 6, 10, 12; and from this work children will learn, firstly, that in modular arithmetic, subtraction, like addition, can always be carried out, whereas in the 'ordinary' set $\{0, 1, 2, 3, . . .\}$, subtraction cannot always be carried out; and, secondly, that subtraction, **unlike** addition, is not commutative, and not associative. They can then be introduced to the idea of an additive inverse, and its use in subtraction:

Additive Inverse.

An additive inverse is a number that has to be added to another number to make a third number, 0.

NUMBER	ADDITIVE INVERSE
1	11
2	10
3	9
4	8
5	7
6	6
7	5
8	4
9	3
10	2
11	1

This is a table showing the additive inverse's in Mod 12.

This shows the additive inverse of 1 which is 11. (in Mod 12)

This clock will help me work out certain addition sums.

Addition.

$7 + 9 = \boxed{4}$

$10 + 6 = \boxed{4}$

$6 + 8 = \boxed{2}$

Subtractions.

$5 - 9 = \boxed{8}$

$3 - 10 = \boxed{5}$

$8 - 11 = \boxed{9}$

There are reverse ways of subtraction.

$\boxed{8} + 9 = 5$

$10 + \boxed{5} = 3$

$\boxed{9} + 11 = 8$

Mod clocks can be used for things such as Mod 7 for days in a week or Mod 12 for hours on a clock.

Write out an addition table for arithmetic mod 5, and find all the pairs of numbers whose sum is equal to 0; for example (1, 4) is such a pair, since $1 + 4 = 0$. Each number in such a pair is called 'the additive inverse' of the other number in the pair; for example, 1 is the additive inverse of 4. Does any number have more than one additive inverse? Is any number its own additive inverse?

Complete the following, so that it shows each number mapped on to its additive inverse mod 5:

$$0 \longrightarrow$$
$$1 \longrightarrow$$
$$2 \longrightarrow 3$$
$$3 \longrightarrow$$
$$4 \longrightarrow 1$$

Find the solutions to the following in mod 5 arithmetic:

$$1 - 4 = \square \qquad 1 + 1 = \square$$
$$1 - 3 = \square \qquad 1 + 2 = \square$$
$$1 - 2 = \square \qquad 1 + 3 = \square$$
$$1 - 1 = \square \qquad 1 + 4 = \square$$
$$1 - 0 = \square \qquad 1 + 0 = \square$$

Notice that the result of subtracting 3 from 1 is the same as that of adding 2 to 1. What can you say about the connection between 2 and 3? Can something similar be said in other cases? Can you write something in the box to make the following open sentence a true statement?

'The result of subtracting any number from 1 is the same as that of adding $\boxed{}$ to 1.'

See if the statement remains true when 1 is replaced by another number.

Throughout this card, the arithmetic is modulo 7.

+	0	1	2	3	4	5	6
0	0	1	2	3	4	5	6
1	1	2	3	4	5	6	0
2	2	3	4	5	6	0	1
3	3	4	5	6	0	1	2
4	4	5	6	0	1	2	3
5	5	6	0	1	2	3	4
6	6	0	1	2	3	4	5

Find the values of $2 - 4$ and $2 + 3$; of $4 - 2$ and $4 + 5$. Can you guess what number should be added to 3 to give the same result as $3 - 6$? Check that your guess was correct.

Find the numbers that should be written in the boxes to make the following true statements:

$$1 - 3 = 1 + \square \qquad 6 - 2 = 6 + \square$$
$$4 - 5 = 4 + \square \qquad 4 - 4 = 4 + \square$$
$$0 - 3 = 0 + \square \qquad 5 - 0 = 5 + \square$$

If the day before yesterday was Tuesday, how many days is it until next Tuesday? Is this question connected with the open sentence: $0 - 2 = 0 + \square$?

From assignments such as these, children should come to see that in modular arithmetic, a number can always be subtracted by adding its additive inverse. In the next section of this Guide, we shall see that the same is true in the arithmetic of the integers.

3. The integers

Many teachers will remember that they themselves as children first met the integers as 'points on a number line', 'directed steps', 'rungs on a ladder', 'marks on a thermometer scale', or in some other physical application. This is the approach adopted in Chapter 4. However, attempts to teach wholly through such applications are in principle unsound, in the sense that they do not help children to form any idea of what integers really are. Furthermore, no single physical application reveals all the properties of the integers: for example, although the applications listed above may be regarded as serving reasonably well as manifestations of **addition**, they become hopelessly confusing as interpretations of **multiplication.** If we teach only physical representations of mathematical entities, rather than present the mathematical entities themselves, the best we can do is to use one representation for one property, quite another for another, and so on.

There is therefore a strong case, **at some stage,** for introducing integers for what they really are, rather than simply in terms of thermometers, etc. So far, with the set of numbers $\{0, 1, 2, 3, \ldots\}$, we have been able to deal with problems like

$$7 = 5 + \square$$

$$8 = 6 + \square$$

$$9 = 7 + \square$$

$$10 = 8 + \square$$

For each of these, the 'solution' is 2, the problems being specified by the pairs of given numbers in each sentence, i.e. (7, 5) for the first, (8, 6) for the second, and so on.

If we now consider instead

$$5 = 7 + \square$$

$$6 = 8 + \square$$

$$7 = 9 + \square$$

$$8 = 10 + \square$$

we would **like** there to be a new 'number' for the solution, the problems now being specified by (5, 7) rather than (7, 5), by (6, 8) instead of (8, 6), and so on. Such a number does not exist in the set $\{0, 1, 2, 3, \ldots\}$ and so a new system must be invented. This will turn out to be the set $\{\ldots, -3, -2, -1, 0, +1, +2, +3, \ldots\}$ that is, the integers. This chapter gives a number of possible approaches, up to addition and subtraction of these new numbers. The other operations, multiplication and division, will be dealt with in a later Guide. Multiplication will be introduced in a number of ways, including an intuitive appeal to the distributive law, and 'ordered pairs' will not be overworked at that stage. But this is still consistent with the view that the very first approach should be to **integers** rather than trickery.

Some teachers may prefer to postpone the present Chapter (and go straight on to Chapter 4). The case for persevering is that a child often returns, when in difficulty, to his **first** impression of a subject: thus, most children brought up to regard integers as 'rungs on a ladder' (which serves well enough for addition) never properly understand multiplication and so their teachers find themselves forced to impose artificial and incomprehensible 'rules' in order to achieve even a minimum standard of competence in mechanical manipulation. And certainly many adults admit that they 'went off' mathematics the day they encountered 'minus times minus makes plus'. Premature questions about $-(-3)$, $-1 \times -1 \times -1$, even $3 - 2 - 4 + 1 - 6$, can lead to a permanent distaste for the subject.

Before any approach is made, some motivation should be given. This will probably include mentioning the ideas given in the first sentence of this Chapter. 'What happens if we want to go below the zero on the thermometer?' 'What about bank overdrafts?' 'How can we cope with $5 = 7 + \triangle$?' And so on. But the point is that we do not at this stage pretend we can answer these questions: we have simply established that there is a need for a new system of numbers, and we will now set about building it.

A possible approach

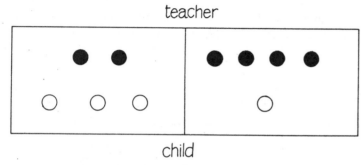

The teacher is armed with a pile of black counters and the child with a pile of white ones. A board is marked off centrally, as shown, into a right-hand and a left-hand side (as viewed by the child, on whom we shall be concentrating). The teacher puts some black counters on each side, but more on the right than the left. The child then places white counters in such a way that the **total** number of counters on each side is the same. In the illustration, he has put 3 on the left and 1 on the right. This could well be recorded as (3, 1). The game for the child is to do this 'total-balancing' in as many ways as possible: **we are not interested in the teacher's counters, but in comparing the various ways in which the child can solve the problem.** Instead of (3, 1), he could for example place (4, 2), (5, 3), (6, 4), etc., or indeed (2, 0). He will by now have recorded a number of ordered pairs,

(2, 0), (3, 1), (4, 2), . . .

and the game can be extended beyond the limit of counters actually available, into the realms of the imagination:
(44, 42), (103, 101), (474, 472), and so on.

Each pair of numbers in the set has the same effect, namely, to win the game with the teacher (by producing the same total on each side of the board). The name of this set should clearly have something to do with '2'.

It may, however, be pointed out straight away that there is another set {(1, 3), (2, 4), (3, 5), (0, 2), . . .} also with certain 'twoness' but nevertheless quite different. For example (1, 3) will **not** be a solution to our original problem

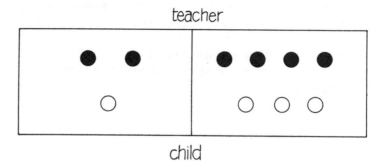

as the total number on both sides is not now the same. Quite arbitrarily,* the set
{(2, 0), (3, 1), (4, 2), . . .} is named +2 (read 'positive two')
and the set
{(0, 2), (1, 3), (2, 4), . . .} is named ⁻2 (read 'negative two').

In the same way the set
(4, 1), (5, 2), (3, 0), . . . is named +3 ('positive three'), and so on.

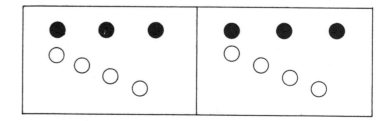

* In fact, some authors name these the other way round.

The teacher can then put the same number of black counters on each side. The child will then come up with the set
{(4, 4), (3, 3), . . .}
including in particular (0, 0) since the totals also balance without any white counters being placed at all. This set is named 0 ('zero').

The rule for determining whether two pairs belong to the same set can be discussed. Two pairs, (a, b) and (c, d), belong to the same set if $a + d = b + c$. For example, (1, 3) and (2, 4) belong to the same set because $1 + 4 = 3 + 2$.

We have by now introduced the integers, $\{. . ., ^-3, ^-2, ^-1, 0, ^+1, ^+2, ^+3 . . .\}$, and the next move is to define 'addition' of these new numbers.

Addition

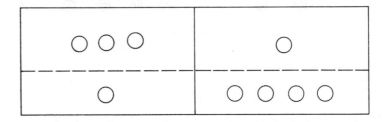

Here the child has represented $^+7$ by the ordered pair (10, 3). By placing the dotted line (or, say, a ruler) this can be shown as (3, 2) and (7, 1). Now (3, 2) represents $^+1$ and (7, 1) represents $^+6$, and it would be pleasant to infer that $^+1 + ^+6 = ^+7$.

However, we must be sure that the 'sum' of $^+1$ and $^+6$ which we get in this way does not depend on the particular pairs we choose to represent them.

Suppose we chose (2, 1) instead of (3, 2) to represent $^+1$, and say (9, 3) instead of (7, 1) for $^+6$. Then, by placing counters on the board, we can see that

these give altogether (11, 4), which again represents $^+7$. The addition of $^+2$ and $^-3$ can be represented, for example,

by (3, 1) and (1, 4), giving altogether (4, 5) which represents $^-1$. But before writing $^+2 + ^-3 = ^+1$, the child must be satisfied that **any** representation of $^+2$ and any representation of $^-3$ will together give a representation of $^-1$. Much practice on these lines should be given, from which the idea of 'addition' of integers can be properly abstracted: 'to add two integers, select an ordered pair representing each and the "combination" (demonstrate on the board) will represent the same integer (as "sum") no matter which particular ordered pairs are chosen from the respective sets'.

Recording might be done as follows:
$$^+1 + ^-4$$
$$\swarrow \qquad \searrow$$
(2, 1) and (0, 4) → (2, 5) → $^-3$
so $^+1 + ^-4 = ^-3$.
(Read → here as 'corresponds to'.)

Numbers That Will Balance (5,3).

I have done these with the equaliser.

(6, 4)
(7, 5)
(9, 7)
(8, 6)

(2, 0)
(4, 2)
(5, 3)
(3, 1)

I have done these without the equaliser.

12, 10	64, 62	19, 17.
13, 11.	70, 68.	21, 19.
20, 18.	40, 38.	23, 21.
100, 98.	15, 13.	98, 96.
90, 88.	29, 27.	200, 198
22, 20.	30, 28.	300, 198.

I know these numbers will balance 5,3. because theres a difference of 2. 9,7 and 8,6 will balance 12,10 2,0 will balance 7,5 and 6,4.

Card 3   <u>Integers and Effects</u>

Here are some of the numbers that
have the same effect as
(0,5)

(5, 10)	(4, 9)	(10, 15)
15, 20	35, 40	50, 55
20, 25	40, 45	200, 205
30, 35	45, 50	55, 60

Here are some of the pairs that
will balance (4, 6)

(6, 8)	(16, 18)	(3, 5)	(60, 62)
10, 12	19, 21	5, 7	64, 66
12, 14	22, 24	100, 102	68, 70

These numbers have the effect 0, 2
because there's two difference and the
lowest number comes first.

Michelle Peters

It is now easy to verify, by means of examples,
 (i) the commutative property, e.g.
$$+1 + -2 = -2 + +1$$
 (ii) the associative property, e.g.
$$(+1 + -3) + +2 = +1 + (-3 + +2).$$

Further, 0 (or 'zero') is the 'neutral element' in the sense that any number is unchanged by adding 0, e.g.
$$+4 + 0 = 0 + +4 = +4$$
and again, each integer has an 'additive inverse' (cf. p. 17), e.g. the additive inverse of $+5$ is -5,
since $+5 + -5 = 0.$

Subtraction

It is now possible to define subtraction in the set of integers. To subtract, for example, $+3$ from $+7$, we find what number when added to $+3$ gives $+7$.
We write $+7 - +3 = +4$
since $+3 + +4 = +7.$

We can now see that we can subtract a number by adding its 'additive inverse' instead (just as with modular arithmetic); e.g.
$$+2 - +1 = +2 + -1 = +1$$
$$+3 - -4 = +3 + +4 = +7$$
$$+7 - +3 = +7 + -3 = +4.$$

Since every integer has an additive inverse, subtraction is always possible.

Several such examples should be analysed. For instance, if $+3 - -4 = \square$, then from our definition
$$-4 + \square = +3$$
so
$$+4 + (-4 + \square) = +4 + +3$$
so
$$(+4 + -4) + \square = +7 \text{ (using the associative property)}$$
so
$$\square = +7$$
i.e. $+3 - -4 = +7$ (so that $+3 - -4 = +3 + +4$).

Other approaches
(i) The equaliser
An equaliser is placed between two children (Arthur and Bill) who sit **facing** each other. Arthur uses a pair of washers of one colour (say, green), while Bill uses a pair of a different colour (say, yellow). One washer of each pair is marked with the word **Starter**, or with 'S'.

When a pair of washers is placed on the equaliser, the 'Starter' is always put on the **left** arm of the balance, the other washer of the pair goes on the right arm.

Arthur sets up a pair of washers like this:

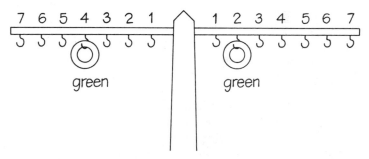

He records (4, 2).
Bill uses his pair of yellow washers to balance Arthur's. Bill must be sure to put his starter on his left as he faces the equaliser.

Arthur records a list of Bill's pairs which balance (4, 2):

(5, 3)
(6, 4)
(7, 5)
(3, 1)
(10, 8)
(2, 0)

The pairs that balance (4, 2) are put into order and a circle is drawn round the 'simplest' version, in this case (2, 0):
{(2, 0), (3, 1), (4, 2), (5, 3), (6, 4) ...}
This set of ordered pairs is named $+2$ (read as 'positive 2').

Arthur and Bill then exchange tasks. Bill sets up a pair of washers and records while Arthur finds the pairs that balance. Additional pairs are added to the list **without** using the equaliser.

e.g. (4, 2) ⟷ (28, 26)

Arthur could then set up two pairs (green and blue, say) with 'starters' on the left. Bill uses one pair to balance the combined effect of Arthur's two pairs,

e.g. (4, 2) and (5, 6) ⟶ (2, 1)
using simplest forms, (2, 0) and (0, 1) ⟶ (1, 0).

The idea then develops as with the 'board and counters' approach.

(ii) Rods

As sets of pairs of natural numbers, the integers are of course quite independent of the board (with its counters) and they may be introduced to children in ways which make no use of it at all. It is possible to **introduce** them as sets of pairs of natural numbers, with no use of apparatus at all, but for most children a physical representation of some kind is very helpful. As an alternative to the board and counters, some teachers prefer to use pairs of rods of different lengths: Cuisenaire rods will serve very well for this purpose. For clarity in the diagrams below, the length of each rod as a multiple of the length of the shortest rod is written on it.

Children can be asked to compare these pairs:

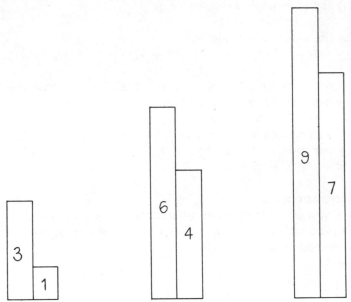

see what they have in common, and how they differ from the pairs:

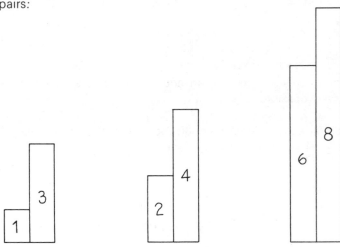

The 'difference' between the '6' and '4' rods can be denoted by (6, 4). 'Differences' such as (2, 0) or (0, 2) can be shown by resting one rod on a flat piece of card, which projects in such a way that the position of the '0' rod can be inferred, ②̲ for (2, 0) and ②̲ for (0, 2).

Adding the Neutral Element

1. $(2,4) + (7,7) = (9,11)$
   $(0,2) + (0,0) = (0,2)$

2. $(7,9) + (6,6) = (13,15)$
   $(0,2) + (0,0) = (0,2)$

3. $(8,5) + (0,0) = (8,5)$
   $(3,0) + (0,0) = (3,0)$

4. $(10,16) + (5,5) = (15,21)$
   $(0,6) + (0,0) = (0,6)$

5. $(3,6) + (10,10) = (13,16)$
   $(0,3) + (0,0) = (0,3)$

Subtraction of Ordered Pairs

1. $(5,0) - (5,2)$
   $(3,2) + (\square\triangle) = (5,0)$
   $(2,3) + (3,2) + (\square\triangle) = (5,0) + (2,3)$
   $(\square\triangle) = (5,0) + (2,3)$
   $(\square\triangle) = (7,3)$
   $= (4,0)$

2. $(5,0) - (1,0)$
   $(1,0) + (\square\triangle) = (5,0)$
   $(0,1) + (1,0) + (\square\triangle) = (5,0) + (0,1)$
   $(\square\triangle) = (5,0) + (0,1)$
   $(\square\triangle) = (5,1)$
   $= (4,0)$

Lina Winder

Addition by Ordered Pairs

$9 + 6 =$ [9 0] + [6 0]

$\quad\quad = $ [15 0]

$\quad\quad = \underline{15}$

$7 + 3 =$ [7 0] + [0 3]

$\quad\quad = $ [7 3]

$\quad\quad = $ [4 0]

$\quad\quad = \underline{4}$

$8 + 5 =$ [0 8] + [0 5]

$\quad\quad = $ [0 13]

$\quad\quad = \underline{13}$

Janice Parsons

The composition of two 'differences' can now be introduced by placing two pairs of rods end-to-end, e.g. (6, 3) and (5, 4) together forming (11, 7).

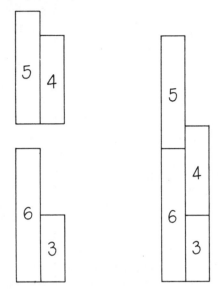

From this point, the treatment can proceed as before, with the integers defined as sets of pairs of natural numbers, and the definition of addition being suggested by, but logically independent of, the behaviour of pairs of rods.

(iii) A variation on the 'board and counters' approach is to

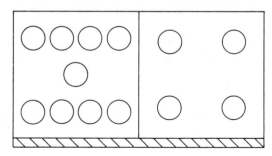

make a set of dominoes ranging from, say, (0, 0) to (10, 10), the illustration showing (9, 4). Each must have a definite 'base' (say a striped area) to separate clearly (9, 4) from (4, 9), etc. The game then is to place one of 'your' dominoes under 'mine' in as many ways as possible, so that the total number of spots on either side of the centre line is the same, e.g.

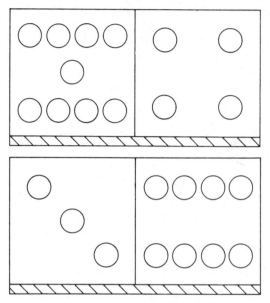

(iv) A simple demonstration that, for example, (3, 2), (2, 1), (1, 0) all represent 1 can be made with a strip of card with notches, as illustrated. The dotted lines represent rubber bands, which can of course be moved suitably to meet at any 'integer' point on the central line.

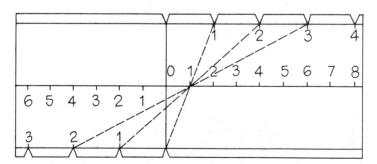

To sum up, the set of integers that we have now got (however they were introduced) consists of the **positive integers** $^+1$, $^+2$, $^+3$, . . .; **zero**, i.e. 0; and the **negative integers** $^-1$, $^-2$, $^-3$, ... In this set

addition is always possible

every member has an additive inverse

subtraction is always possible, and is equivalent to the addition of the additive inverse.

$^-2 - {}^-3$ means the integer which when added to $^-3$ gives $^-2$; this is $^+1$ (because $^-3 + {}^+1 = {}^-2$). The additive inverse of $^-3$ is $^+3$ (because $^-3 + {}^+3 = 0$), and $^-2 + {}^+3 = {}^+1$, so $^-2 - {}^-3 = {}^-2 +$ (additive inverse of $^-3$).

To subtract one integer, for example $^+1$, from a second, for example $^+3$, is to find what integer when added to the first, $^+1$, gives the second, $^+3$;
$^+3 - {}^+1 = {}^+2$ because $^+1 + {}^+2 = {}^+3$.

With integers, we can always subtract by adding the additive inverse: the additive inverse of $^+2$ is $^-2$ because $^+2 + {}^-2 = 0$. What is the additive inverse of $^-2$, $^-3$, $^+1$, $^+4$, 0?

We can therefore find $^+4 - {}^-1$ **either** by completing $^-1 + \square = {}^+4$ **or** by finding the additive inverse of $^-1$ (which is $^+1$) and adding it to $^+4$. Find the result of each of the following subtractions in both of these ways. Do you find that sometimes one way is easier, and sometimes the other?

$^+3 - {}^+2$	$^+5 - 0$
$^-3 - {}^-1$	$0 - {}^-5$
$^-3 - {}^+1$	$^-1 - {}^-1$
$^+4 - {}^-3$	$^+3 - {}^-3$

It is now clear that, in the set of integers, there are many results very similar to results in the set of numbers $\{0, 1, 2, 3, . . .\}$; for example, under addition, two positive integers (and two negative integers) behave just like the corresponding natural numbers.

We have
$^+2 + {}^+5 = {}^+7$ (positive integers)
$^-2 + {}^-5 = {}^-7$ (negative integers)
$2 + 5 = 7$ (natural numbers)

Under subtraction, too, some results on positive integers, and some on negative integers, are just like results on corresponding natural numbers.

We have
$^+5 - {}^+2 = {}^+3$ (positive integers)
$^-5 - {}^-2 = {}^-3$ (negative integers)
$5 - 2 = 3$ (natural numbers)

However, we also have
$^+2 - {}^+5 = {}^-3$
$^-2 - {}^-5 = {}^+3$

whilst there is no natural number equal to $2 - 5$.

Later on, when we have studied multiplication of integers (not in this Guide) we shall find that under multiplication and division two positive integers, though **not** two negative integers, also behave like the two corresponding natural numbers, and from that point, we shall not find it necessary to distinguish between positive integers and natural numbers, and we shall always be able to use positive integers in place of natural numbers. Even now, while we are still distinguishing positive integers from natural numbers, we can use the integers to help with the problem of subtraction in the set $\{0, 1, 2, 3, . . .\}$.

It is clear from what we have seen above that if we know that $^+43 - {}^+17 = {}^+26$, then we also know that $43 - 17 = 26$. Now some of the difficulties associated with subtracting 17 from 43, such as '7 from 3 I can't', do not appear when $^+17$ is subtracted from $^+43$; for example, $^+7$ can be subtracted from $^+3$. In fact, we have:

$^+43 - {}^+17 = {}^+43 + {}^-17$ (because subtraction is equivalent to addition of the additive inverse)

$= ({}^+40 + {}^+3) + ({}^-10 + {}^-7)$ ($43 = 40 + 3$, so $^+43 = {}^+40 + {}^+3$; $17 = 10 + 7$, so $^-17 = {}^-10 + {}^-7$)

$= ({}^+40 + {}^-10) + ({}^+3 + {}^-7)$ (because addition of integers is commutative and associative)

$= ({}^+40 - {}^+10) + ({}^+3 - {}^+7)$

$= {}^+30 + {}^-4$

$= {}^+26$

The Integers.

Carolyn Hague

This is a table for Integers. All the Integers under the arrow going in a negative direction begin with minus like minus three.

All the Integers under the arrow going in a positive direction begin with plus something such as plus three.

$^-3 - \boxed{^+5} = ^+2$

$^+2 + \square = ^-5$ In this sum we start off with $^+2$. Then we

$^+2 + \boxed{^-7} = ^-5$ add something on and we get $^-5$. We must find what we add on. We can use our table to help us. We find plus two and we find minus five and then we count up from the two to the five and we

$^-4 - \boxed{^+2} = ^-2$ get seven. But what kind of seven?

$^-2 + \square = ^+4$ Well we counted up in a negative

$^-2 + \boxed{^+2} = ^-4$ direction so it must be minus seven. We work out all our sums like that.

$^+3 - ^+2 = \boxed{^+1}$ $^-3 - ^-2 = \square$

$^+2 + \boxed{^+1} = ^+3$ $^-2 + \square = ^-3$

          $^-2 + \boxed{^-1} = ^-3$

Elaine Wiggan.

Integers

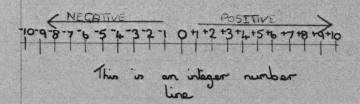

This is an integer number
line

We can write subtraction problems
as addition in integers like these.

$$^-4 - {}^-2 = \boxed{^-2}$$
$$^-2 + \boxed{^-2} = ^-4$$

$$^+3 - {}^+2 = \boxed{^+1}$$
$$^+2 + \boxed{^+1} = ^+3$$

$$^-3 - {}^-2 = \boxed{^-1}$$
$$^-2 + \boxed{^-1} = ^-3$$

$$^-10 - {}^+10 = \boxed{^-20}$$
$$^+10 + \boxed{^-20} = ^-10$$

$$0 - {}^+3 = \boxed{^-3}$$
$$^+3 + \boxed{^-3} = 0$$

We can do this by turning it round
and saying what must I add to
$^+3$ to make 0   Ans $^-3$

The first four lines of the above argument show that the tens and units can be treated separately, and when children understand why this is so, they can set out the whole process shortly, as follows:

Subtract

tens	units
+4	+3
+1	+7
+3	−4

This means we have +30 + −4, i.e. +26.

Assignments such as the following (page 36) can be given to the children:

You will have noticed that some pairs of integers add, and subtract, just like the corresponding natural numbers.

For example,
$^+5 + {}^+3 = {}^+8$ (positive integers)
$^-5 + {}^-3 = {}^-8$ (negative integers)
may be compared with
$5 + 3 = 8$ (natural numbers)
and
$^+5 - {}^+3 = {}^+2$ (positive integers)
$^-5 - {}^-3 = {}^-2$ (negative integers)
may be compared with
$5 - 3 = 2$ (natural numbers)

For each of the following results, can you find an exactly similar result about the natural numbers? For which can you **not** find a similar result?
$^+5 + {}^+1 = {}^+6$
$^+5 + 0 = {}^+5$
$^+3 - {}^+1 = {}^+2$
$^-3 + {}^-1 = {}^-4$
$^-3 - {}^-1 = {}^-2$
$^-3 + {}^+1 = {}^-2$
$^-1 + {}^-1 = {}^-2$
$^+3 - {}^+4 = {}^-1$
$^-3 - {}^-4 = {}^+1$
$^-3 - 0 = {}^-3$

For each of the following results about natural numbers, write down two results about integers which are exactly like it:
$4 + 3 = 7$
$4 - 3 = 1$
$4 + 0 = 4$
$2 - 2 = 0$

Can you find any result about natural numbers for which there are no similar results for integers?

You will remember that we were led to invent the integers because some subtractions could not be carried out in the set of numbers $\{0, 1, 2, \ldots\}$. We still cannot subtract the natural number 3 from the natural number 2, but the positive integers $^+3$ and $^+2$ behave exactly like 3 and 2 when we add them, when we subtract $^+2$ from $^+3$ and, as we shall see later, when we multiply them; and we **can** subtract $^+3$ from $^+2$:

$$^+2 - {}^+3 = {}^-1$$

It is in this way that we have solved our original problem: by inventing new numbers, the integers, which will do all that the natural numbers will do, and also are such that any one of them can be subtracted from any other.

In the natural numbers, there is nothing that can be written in the boxes to make the following true statements (the open sentences have empty truth-sets):

$$3 - 5 = \boxed{}$$

$$0 - 4 = \boxed{}$$

$$6 + \boxed{} = 2$$

$$\boxed{} + 7 = 0$$

Replace the natural numbers by positive integers, and complete each of the statements. The first has been done for you:

$$^+3 - {}^+5 = \boxed{{}^-2}$$

Because the positive integers behave just like natural numbers, we can use them to help us with subtraction problems involving natural numbers larger than 10.

Can you find $84 - 38$?

Let us find instead $^+84 - {}^+38$.

$$
\begin{aligned}
{}^+84 - {}^+38 &= {}^+84 + {}^-38 \quad \text{(why?)}\\
&= ({}^+80 + {}^+4) + ({}^-30 + {}^-8) \quad \text{(how do we know?)}\\
&= ({}^+80 + {}^-30) + ({}^+4 + {}^-8) \quad \text{(why?)}\\
&= ({}^+80 - {}^+30) + ({}^+4 - {}^+8)\\
&= {}^+50 + {}^-4\\
&= {}^+46
\end{aligned}
$$

And so $84 - 38 = 46$.

Discuss with your teacher how you might set out the working for $^+84 - {}^+38$ more shortly.

Use this method to find $63 - 37$, $90 - 36$, $88 - 25$, $265 - 148$.

Subtraction

Subtraction has now been introduced on a proper footing: the operation is always possible using the set of integers. By this stage, the children have a firm basis which should enable them to cope with understanding. The case for postponing subtraction for so long is strong, but it is also novel, so that it may be worth recalling the reasons for this. The following is quoted from *Computation and Structure* ❸:

A note on subtraction

This operation has been delayed as long as possible, which may surprise many teachers, but it has to be thought about very seriously indeed because it presents difficulties to children which may be easily overlooked. The many 'techniques' employed in teaching subtraction are felt to be one of the reasons why, later on, there is so much confusion when the negative integers are encountered.

Literal 'taking-away' is of course a very early activity, but there is a long way to go from this process of physical removal to the understanding of the mathematical operation of subtraction. Major difficulties arise from the non-associativity, e.g.

$$12 - (6 - 4) \neq (12 - 6) - 4$$

and also non-commutativity, e.g. $7 - 5 \neq 5 - 7$

Recording and using 'rules' for subtraction is where the trouble usually begins. Can we, for instance, try to remove some of the jargon which goes with traditional 'subtraction' sums, e.g.

'3 from 2, you can't'
'Borrow 1 and pay 1 back'?

It has already been mentioned in *Computation and Structure* that most problems involving subtraction can be solved much more sensibly by using complementary addition, e.g. $47 - 39$ means 'what must be added to 39 to reach 47?'; i.e. $39 + \square = 47$. In practical situations met with in the classroom, with the use of block charts perhaps, to the child's own way of thinking it is by addition (complementary addition) that subtraction will be more readily seen and handled, e.g.

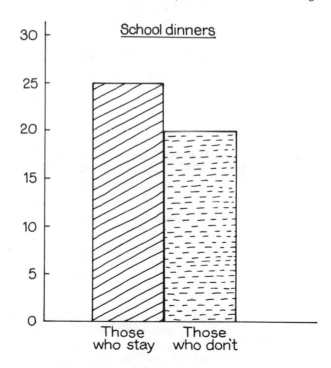

School dinners

From such situations many problems arising will involve 'differences':

How many more?

How many less?

By comparison the children 'add on' to solve the problems, as do most people when faced with everyday problems of this kind. It does seem, therefore, that we impose subtraction techniques on children when there is no need for it.

At a later stage, the 'superior plus' symbol can be omitted, for example $^+3$ being written simply as 3. $^+4 - {}^+3$ could be written as $4 - 3$, the context showing that the work is in the set of integers rather than natural numbers. $^+4 + {}^-3$ is equal to $^+4 - {}^+3$ and so could also be written as $4 - 3$.

It would then be possible to set out subtraction in hybrid fashion:

$$\begin{array}{r} 85 \\ -\ 27 \\ \hline 60 + (^-2) \\ = 58 \end{array}$$

(This is a shorthand for $^+85 - {}^+27 = {}^+60 + {}^-2 = {}^+58$.)

$$\begin{array}{r} \text{Subtract} \\ 4 \quad {}^{1}2 \\ 1_1 \quad 8 \\ \hline 2 \quad 4 \end{array}$$

In this method, we are saying $42 - 18 = (40 + 2) - (10 + 8) = (40 + 12) - (20 + 8) = (40 - 20 + (12 - 8) = 20 + 4$. This method is clearly more sophisticated (and appears less natural, when illustrated by structural material such as Dienes blocks) than that of decomposition.

However, it may be very useful in cases such as

$$\begin{aligned} 104 - 88 &= 114 - 98 \\ &= 116 - 100 \\ &= 16 \\ \text{or } 641 - 399 &= 642 - 400 \\ &= 242 \end{aligned}$$

The method can be demonstrated with rods:

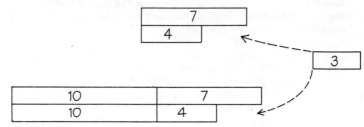

The addition of the **same length** to both rods can be **seen** to leave the difference as before.

The important thing is that these 'techniques' should be taken apart and discussed with real understanding. Occasionally the process should be written out in some detail, e.g.

$$\begin{aligned} &301 - 17 \\ =\ &301 + {}^-17 \\ =\ &300 + 1 + {}^-10 + {}^-7 \\ =\ &(300 + {}^-10) + (1 + {}^-7) \\ =\ &290 + {}^-6 \\ =\ &284 \end{aligned}$$

The re-grouping $(300 + {}^-10) + (1 + {}^-7)$ is permissible since **addition** is associative and commutative. It is as well to emphasise that subtraction is not associative or commutative, e.g.

$$\begin{aligned} &(10 - 7) - 1 = 2 \\ \text{but } &10 - (7 - 1) = 4 \\ \text{and } &10 - 7 \neq 7 - 10 \end{aligned}$$

Even when subtracting 17 from 301, children may still prefer complementary addition, the remarks in parentheses not being recorded.

At this stage, too, the 'usual' methods of subtraction can be introduced and analysed. (Again we are really dealing with integers, but without 'superior plus' symbols.)

For example,

$$\begin{aligned} 42 - 18 &= (30 + 12) - (10 + 8) \\ &= (30 - 10) + (12 - 8) \end{aligned}$$

This may be demonstrated using counters (cf. *Computation and Structure* ❸ from which the following is also reproduced) and leads to one of the usual techniques ('decomposition'), which it then becomes feasible to set out as

$$
\begin{array}{cc}
3 & 12 \\
\cancel{4} & \cancel{2} \\
-1 & 8 \\
\hline
2 & 4 \\
\hline
\end{array}
$$

It is clearer to set out as shown, rather than to cross out only the '4' in 42:

$$
\begin{array}{cc}
3 & 1 \\
4 & 2 \\
-1 & 8 \\
\hline
2 & 4 \\
\hline
\end{array}
$$

Dienes blocks will help greatly towards an understanding of the process just described. If 42 is represented by 4 longs and 2 unit blocks, 1 long has to be exchanged for 10 units before blocks representing 18 can be matched, or removed. It is very desirable for work of this kind to be carried out in different bases.

> Some teachers may like to explore the connection with modular arithmetic. The 'units' digits in any sum in base 6, for example, are the numbers in a sum in arithmetic modulo 6, e.g.
>
> in base 6,
> $$
> \begin{array}{r}
> 15 \\
> 24 \\
> \hline
> 43 \\
> \hline
> \end{array}
> $$
> (the 15 standing for $(1 \times 6) + 5$, etc.). Here $5 + 4 = 13$, i.e. $(1 \times 6) + 3$. Now, on the contrary, in mod 6 arithmetic, we literally ignore multiples of 6, and are concerned only with 'remainders', so that $5 + 4 = 3 \pmod 6$.

Other procedures for solving a problem such as $42 - 18 = \square$ should be investigated. Thus by adding 2 to both 42 and 18, we obtain $44 - 20 = 24$; again, children need experience in taking away, and matching to see that $a - b$ is unaltered if a and b are both increased (or decreased) by the same number. This fact is of course the basis for the method of subtraction known as 'equal additions':

$$
\begin{array}{lr}
17 \text{ (to 20 is)} & 3 \\
(20 \text{ to } 100 \text{ is}) & 80 \\
(100 \text{ to } 301 \text{ is}) & 201 \\
\hline
& 284 \\
\hline
\end{array}
$$

$$
\text{Check:} \quad
\begin{array}{r}
284 \\
+ 17 \\
\hline
301 \\
\hline
\end{array}
$$

This is quicker than it looks.

To summarise,

(a) Formal subtraction should not be tackled too soon, but the idea of 'making up to', i.e. complementary addition, is bound to crop up and should be encouraged.

(b) In the past, too much mumbo-jumbo (namely, 'borrow ten and pay it back', 'give it ten', 'one in the attic and one on the doorstep') has tended to obscure what would otherwise have been good methods. (Perhaps these methods have been 'over-taught but under-learned'.)

(c) Too much stress has been put on '**the** method of subtraction' instead of allowing time to take methods apart (preferably using some apparatus, Dienes, Cuisenaire, etc.) and giving children the opportunity of selecting their own method.

Perhaps the most important thing is that the children should be free to choose their own methods and then be prepared to justify them.

4 Applications of the integers

In *Computation and Structure* ❷ the numbers 0, 1, 2, . . . were used to label equally-spaced points on a horizontal line extending indefinitely to the right.

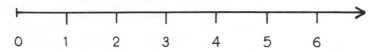

One use·of the integers, which are defined in Chapter 3, is to label points on a horizontal line extending indefinitely both to the right and to the left:

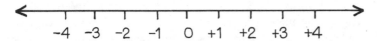

Indeed, if we wish to label points on such a line, the **symbols** for the integers can be introduced for this purpose (and also for labelling points on a lattice, as suggested in *Graphs Leading to Algebra* ❷, Chapter 5) before any study of the integers themselves. Very often, however, the possibility of doing this has led teachers to omit any discussion of the kind to which the last Chapter is devoted, and while this may lead more rapidly to worth-while applications of the integers, it is strongly recommended, for the reasons set out at the beginning of Chapter 3, that that Chapter should be studied, and used, before the present one.

However, the number line is certainly convenient as a representation of the integers, and can be used to give a simple definition of the relations $>$ and $<$ between integers, as suggested in the following card:

What do you think the letters R and L stand for in this diagram?

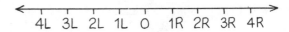

Can you suggest other symbols for labelling the points on the line? We shall use the symbols for the integers . . . $^-4$, $^-3$, $^-2$, $^-1$, 0, $^+1$, $^+2$, $^+3$, $^+4$, . . .

The diagram makes it easy to decide when one integer is to be called 'greater than' another. In this diagram, the greater of two

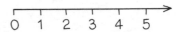

numbers labels the point farther to the right. So we say one integer is 'greater than' a second if the point labelled by the first is to the

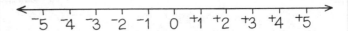

right of the point labelled by the second; and then the second integer is called 'less than' the first. As between natural numbers, we write '$>$' for 'greater than' and '$<$' for 'less than'.

Put the correct sign, $>$, or $<$, between the following pairs of integers (the first has been done for you):

$^+5$	$>$	$^-2$	$^-1$	0
$^+5$		$^+1$	$^-2$	$^-3$
$^+3$		0	$^-3$	$^+4$
$^+1$		$^+2$	$^-100$	$^+10$

To understand fully how addition is represented on the number line, it is important to see that integers can be used, not only to label points on the line, but also to refer to movements along the line from one point to another (compare the representations of numbers in modular arithmetic as points on a clock, and as movement of a clock hand). +2 can be represented by a movement on the number line of 2 positions to the right (e.g from +5 to +7, from −3 to −1, from −1 to +1, etc.) ; −2 by a movement on the number line of 2 positions to the left (e.g. from +7 to +5, from −1 to −3, from +1 to −1, etc.).

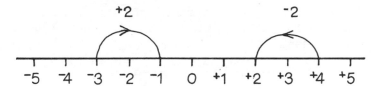

This interpretation of integers as movements on the number line lends itself well to an interpretation of addition as 'followed by' (or 'and then'). +2 + +3 may be interpreted as 'a movement of 2 to the right (beginning in any position), **followed by** a movement of 3 to the right': this is clearly equivalent to 'a movement of 5 to the right', i.e. +5.

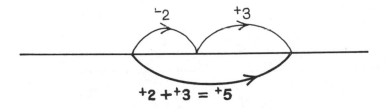

+2 + −6 is 'a movement of 2 to the right, **and then** a movement of 6 to the left', which is clearly equivalent to 'a movement of 4 to the left', i.e. −4.

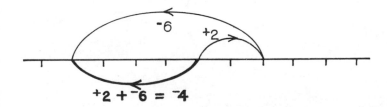

In this interpretation of the integers, the points do not need to be labelled, and we can begin at any point. If the points **are** labelled, one diagram representing +2 + +3 = +5 is where the first movement begins at 0.

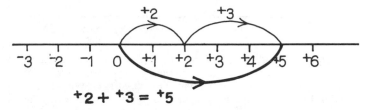

If the arrows representing movements from 0 are omitted, it is clear that all the integers appearing in +2 + +3 = +5 are still indicated in the simpler diagram.

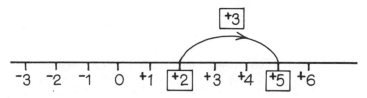

With this diagram, +2 + +3 + +5 can be represented as follows : 'If we begin at the point +2, and then move 3 to the right, we finish at the point +5'. This representation of an addition is easy to use, but because the +2 and +5 are represented by **points** on the number line and the +3 as a **movement** along it, it is not really as simple as it seems. For this reason, it is recommended that children should be introduced to addition on the number line through the interpretation of **all** the integers appearing in a sum such as +2 + +3 = +5, as movements. (There is unfortunately no simple way of interpreting **all** the integers appearing in such a sum as points.)

We can also represent integers as movements along a number line.

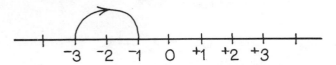

Let us represent ⁺2 by a movement from **any** labelled point on the line to the point 2 positions to the right (one such movement is shown by an arrow in the diagram). What movement do you think we should represent ⁺3 by? ⁻3? Beginning at any point on the line, move 2 to the right (let us say 'move ⁺2'), and then move ⁺3:

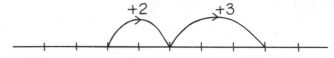

Notice how we can represent these movements on a number line without labelling the points. What single movement would be equivalent to first moving ⁺2 and then moving ⁺3? Would it be reasonable to write ⁺2 + ⁺3 for this? Try some more pairs of movements, for example, ⁺2 + ⁻3:

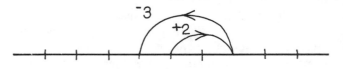

What single movement is this equivalent to?

Show movements to represent:
⁺2 + ⁺1 = ⁺3
⁺1 + ⁻3 = ⁻2
⁺2 + 0 = ⁺2
⁻1 + ⁻2 = ⁻3

Use the number line to solve:
⁺5 + ⁻8 = ☐
⁻2 + ⁺2 = ☐
⁻3 + ⁻3 = ☐
⁺1 + ⁻2 + ⁺4 = ☐
⁺2 + ⁻3 + ⁺5 + ⁻1 = ☐

What happens if you begin your first movement at the point labelled 0? What can you say about the point at which the last movement ends?

It is worth noticing that both the commutativity and associativity of addition of integers are very clear from the movement interpretation:

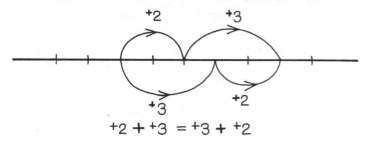

$$^+2 + {}^+3 = {}^+3 + {}^+2$$

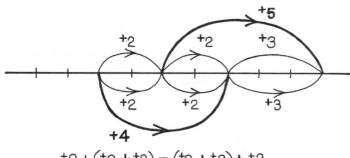

$$^+2 + \left({}^+2 + {}^+3\right) = \left({}^+2 + {}^+2\right) + {}^+3$$

Children will probably need more practice with examples like these.

It is worth drawing similar diagrams to illustrate associativity with three integers, one or two of which are negative.

Since
+4 − +6 = □.
is equivalent to
+6 + □ = +4
+4 − +6 may be interpreted as the movement needed after a movement of +6 (6 to the right) to give a result equivalent to a movement of +4 (4 to the right).

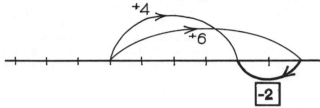

This is clearly −2.
In this case, if the movements representing +6 and +4 began at the point 0, both the integers which are **given** in the problem
+4 − +6 = □
could be regarded as represented by **points** on the line, and the result of the subtraction shown by the **movement** needed to go from +6 to +4

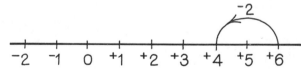

When children can handle addition using the dual interpretation of integers as positions and as movements, they may be able to handle subtraction in this way.

Can you solve the following (without using the number line) ?

+5 − +3 = □
+2 − ⁻3 = □
+4 − +7 = □
⁻1 − +2 = □
⁻1 − ⁻3 = □

In each case, consider what movement along the number line would be needed to go from the number being subtracted to the number from which it is subtracted: for example, in the first problem above, to go from +3 to +5.

Can you find how to carry out subtraction using the number line? Make up some more problems for yourself.

Try to see why what you do works by changing some of your subtractions into statements involving addition instead.

So far, we have used the number line only in a horizontal position, with the positive integers appearing to the right of 0. But of course the line may appear and be used in any position: it may even be more familiar to children in a vertical position, for they may have noticed the scale on a thermometer. On a thermometer scale, the + sign is usually omitted with the positive integers, and a different colour instead of the sign ⁻ may be used to distinguish temperatures below zero from those above. This is well worth discussing with the class; but in the following assignment, + and ⁻ signs are used in the usual way.

Positive and negative integers are used on a Celsius (formerly termed centigrade) thermometer to measure temperatures above and below zero. A reading of ⁻5 represents 5 degrees below zero, and a reading of ⁺50 represents 50 degrees above zero.

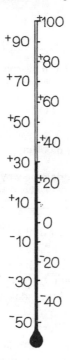

Is there any real difference between a thermometer scale and a number line?

During one year, the temperature on the hottest day reached ⁺50 degrees, and on the coldest day it fell to ⁻12 degrees. What was the difference between these temperatures?

On a certain day, the temperature at 9 a.m. was ⁺5 degrees; it rose 10 degrees between 9 a.m. and 12 noon, 2 degrees further between 2 p.m. and 5 p.m. What was the temperature at 5 p.m.?

Make up a similar problem to illustrate
$$^+10 + {^+5} + {^-8} = {^+7}$$

Notice how the integers can be used to refer not only to temperatures but also to changes of temperature: ⁻5 can be used to refer to a **fall** in temperature of 5 degrees as well as to a temperature of ⁻5 degrees.

What does the thermometer in the diagram read?
What does your classroom or school thermometer read?
How is 'freezing point' marked?
What do you think ⁻10 degrees Celsius means?
How many degrees would the reading on the above thermometer have to fall to reach:
a freezing point,
b ⁻10 degrees,
c ⁺20 degrees,
d ⁻30 degrees?
Which is colder, ⁻10 degrees or ⁻20 degrees?
Is it true that ⁻10 < ⁻20 or that ⁻20 < ⁻10?
Which is warmer, ⁺10 degrees or ⁺20 degrees?
Is it true that ⁺10 > ⁺20 or that ⁺20 > 10?
Is ⁻5 degrees a higher temperature than ⁻10 degrees?
What change in temperature must occur to raise the temperature from ⁺10 degrees to ⁺15 degrees? What is the connection between the last question and the problem ⁺15 − ⁻10 = □?

Today is my birthday and I got £5 of my mom and dad. I put the money in the bank. Aswell as that I won £10 on the pools. Then I had to spend £3 on a trip to Heysham Head. Then I bought my mom a birthday present for £2. Now I have £10 left. This is an aqustion to show how much he has got left. £5 + £$^+$10 + £$^-$3 + £$^-$2 = £$^+$10

The dual interpretation of integers, as describing both positions, or states, and changes of position, or state, extends to all their applications, in particular to credits and debits. It is convenient, for example, to use £ $^+2$ to refer both to a credit balance of £2 in a banking account, and to a deposit of £2. The following assignment deals with this situation. Notice that we must distinguish carefully between $^+3 + {}^-2$ and $^+3 - {}^+2$; it is not, in fact, particularly easy to interpret subtraction in the application of the integers to credits and debits, and some teachers may prefer to consider only addition.

An alternative approach, in which a postman delivers cheques and bills, and collects cheques and bills delivered in error, is worked out very fully in the books published by the American Madison Project, especially in *Discovery in Mathematics* by Robert B. Davis, and teachers are strongly recommended to refer to this book.

We can use the integers to represent deposits and withdrawals, in pounds for example, in a banking account, by agreeing to use positive integers to represent deposits and negative integers to represent withdrawals.

If a man made a deposit of £10, and then another of £10, we could represent his total deposits by $^+10 + {}^+10$. If then he made a withdrawal of £5, the total change in his account could be represented by $^+10 + {}^+10 + {}^-5 = {}^+15$, and so would be equivalent to that made by a single deposit of £15.

We may also represent his total balance at the bank by a positive integer if he in fact has money in his account (a credit balance), and by a negative integer if he owes the bank money (in this last case, his account is sometimes said to be 'in the red' because bank statements of money owing to the bank are often written in red).

If a man's account has a credit balance of £50, he deposits £20, withdraws £30, and finally deposits £20, what is his balance after his last deposit?

Make up a story to illustrate:
$^+20 + {}^+30 + {}^-50$

If your bank statement shows a balance (in £s) of $^+40$, and the bank discovers that it has wrongly credited you with a deposit of £10, your correct balance could be shown as $^+40 - {}^+10 = {}^+30$.

Make up a story to illustrate:
$^-10 + {}^+20 + {}^+30 - {}^-20 + {}^-10 - {}^+40 = \square$

Integers can also be used to refer to water flowing into or out of a tank, to dates B.C. and A.D., to distances, or movements, East and West, or North and South, and to heights above and below sea-level. All these examples are suitable for children as illustrations of the use of integers. A map which includes both land and sea often has contours giving heights above sea-level in feet, and depths below sea-level in fathoms, and can be used to suggest problems in which account must be taken of this difference of units before integers are introduced as measures of height and depth.

Two other suggestions for assignments are the following:

A boy was watching a rocket-launching on television. As the announcer said 'Blast-off minus 5 seconds' he watched carefully and the pictures below show what he saw on the television screen. (We have said 'negative 5' instead of 'minus 5'.)

-5	-4	-3	-2	-1	BLAST-OFF	+1	+2	+3	+4	+5

What symbol could you use for 'blast-off'?

The last picture shows the count at +5 seconds. After the boy had watched for 5 more seconds, what count was shown on the screen?

What was the count 3 seconds before 'blast-off'?

What was the count 3 seconds before that?

What was the count 4 seconds after 'blast-off' and 3 seconds before that?

From 5 seconds before 'blast-off' how long had the boy been watching when the screen showed +7?

What do you understand by a 'count-down'?

+7	-7	-6	+4
-4	+2	+1	-1
	-2		+3
	+5	+6	

What is the sum of the integers in the first row of the above table? What is the sum of the integers in the second row, and what is the sum of the integers in the second column?

Can you fill in the empty spaces with integers so that every row, every column, and each of the two diagonals has the same total?

You have made a 'magic square' using integers instead of natural numbers.

Can you make a magic square of 3 rows and 3 columns using the integers -2, -1, 0, +1, +2, +3, +4, +5, +6? What would the sum of each row, column and diagonal have to be? Try to decide what integer to put in the central position first.

Graphical work using the integers is dealt with fully in *Graphs Leading to Algebra* 2 , and much of the work in that Guide can be done at the same time as the work of the present section. The following assignments suggest some very simple graphical work relating to two of the uses of the integers referred to above.

For a period of 6 months, temperatures in degrees Celsius at noon and midnight were recorded at a weather station, and the highest noon temperature, and the lowest midnight temperature for each month were as given here:

month	1	2	3	4	5	6
highest noon temperature	+8	+9	+12	+20	+21	+18
lowest midnight temperature	-10	-6	-2	+4	+6	+7

Using a horizontal axis labelled with the numbers 1 to 6, and a vertical axis labelled with integers, as shown,

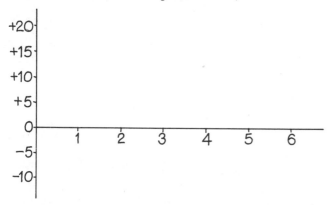

plot points to show these temperatures. Join the points showing the lowest temperatures with a dotted line, and those showing the highest temperatures with another. Why not continuous lines? What were the highest, and lowest, temperatures recorded?

Between which two consecutive months did the highest noon temperature change most?
In which month was there the greatest difference between the highest noon temperature and the lowest midnight temperature?

In the centre of London, the ground is approximately 100 feet above sea-level. The table below gives the approximate height in feet above sea-level, or depth below sea-level, of the ground at five points due East, and five points due West, of London; a height above sea-level of 50 feet is indicated by +50, a depth below sea-level of 50 feet by -50.

	West of London					East of London				
distance from London (in miles)	500	400	300	200	100	100	200	300	200	500
height above or below sea-level	-2000	-400	-250	-200	+700	-300	+50	+500	+2000	+1000

How could you use integers to represent the distances from London?

Using horizontal and vertical axes labelled with integers, crossing at the point labelled 0 on each of them, as shown,

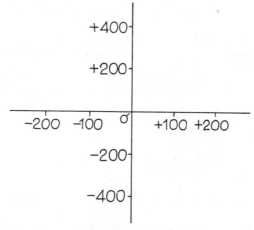

plot points to show the information given above. How should the axes be labelled? Do you think the points you have plotted could be joined by a curve? Find from an atlas where are the places 200 miles due East, and 200 miles due West, of London.

5 Large numbers and indices

Large numbers fascinate many children in this space and technological age. Our main task as teachers seems to be to help children understand and 'read' them. Discussion concerning large numbers should take place in an informal way; the various ways in which they appear, or are used, will inevitably arise and, no doubt, information on space, the solar system, populations, etc., will be explored. Perhaps the first task will be to convey a 'feeling' for the size of, say, a million. To make a start, a class discussion might begin with something like the following:

'We count eggs in dozens; football crowds in thousands; pages of a book in hundreds; populations of most cities and towns in hundreds of thousands: can you think of anything which we count in millions?'

The following information can be discussed and may be of use to teachers who wish to excite children's curiosity regarding the use of large numbers. Of course, children should also be encouraged and set to find out their own facts and figures.

When a start has been made it will soon be evident that children now need to be given a review of the principles of our system of place value but, before we embark on this, it would be useful to present them with some idea of what a million looks like.

The sea contains over 300 million (300,000,000) cubic miles of water. There are billions of plants and animals in the sea.

The Earth's surface (land and sea) is approximately 196,950,000 (one hundred and ninety-six million, nine hundred and fifty thousand) square miles.

The approximate areas (in square miles) of the oceans of the world are as follows:

Pacific	68,802,000
Atlantic	31,530,000
Arctic	5,440,000
Indian	28,356,000
Antarctic	5,731,000

Put these in order of size, starting with the largest ocean.

The Great Pyramid in Egypt was built by the Pharaoh Cheops. It took 100,000 slaves 20 years and required approximately 2,300,000 huge stones to complete it.

Have a look at a million

A million is a very large number and it is difficult for you to see or count a million of anything.

Can you think of any way of doing this?

One way would be to get a piece of graph paper which is marked off in 1-inch and $\frac{1}{10}$-inch squares.

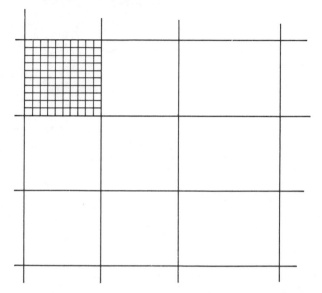

How many little $\frac{1}{10}$-inch squares are there in a 1-inch square?
How many little $\frac{1}{10}$-inch squares are there in 10 1-inch squares?
How many little $\frac{1}{10}$-inch squares are there in 100 1-inch squares?
How many little $\frac{1}{10}$-inch squares are there in 1000 1-inch squares?
How many little $\frac{1}{10}$-inch squares are there in 10,000 1-inch squares?

How many sheets of graph paper would you need to show this? Could you put them on your classroom wall?

Another way would be to count out a million grains of rice, lentils, barley, etc. You could get very near to a million (an approximation) without actually counting all of them. Can you think how you might do this? (Scales may help you!)

The small and large cubes contained in the Dienes apparatus (Base 10) might give you an idea of showing a million.

After a suitable revision of place value up to, say, 1000, which, by now, most children will be able to understand fairly easily, they can be asked to consider further places to the left (in Base 10). Care will now be needed to stress the way we 'read' millions and thousands in terms of 1, 10 and 100, e.g.
we can have
   1 thousand
  10 thousand
100 thousand
   1 million
  10 million
100 million

A 'visual aid' for illustrating this might look like the following:

number of millions			number of thousands			number of ones		
100's	10's	1's	100's	10's	1's	100's	10's	1's
⊙⊙	⊙⊙ ⊙⊙ ⊙⊙	⊙⊙ ⊙⊙	⊙⊙ ⊙⊙ ⊙	⊙⊙ ⊙	⊙	⊙⊙ ⊙⊙ ⊙⊙ ⊙	⊙⊙ ⊙⊙ ⊙⊙ ⊙⊙ ⊙	⊙⊙
2	6	4	5	3	1	7	9	2

This would be all the more attractive to children if the pins in the panels were light bulbs and actually lit up, but they can be just pins or pegs on which we could hang washers or coloured beads. In any case, the children can be asked to think of this as the 'Large Number Machine' and assignments like the following could be tried out – probably as a class activity for a beginning:

This is a machine for dealing with large numbers. It is used to 'remember' these large numbers for us. The number on the machine at present is shown by the 'lights' (or washers). Notice that the 'lights' are in panels of 3. There are 3 panels for the millions, 3 for the thousands and 3 for the ones.

How many lights does each panel have?
Why this many?
What number base does the machine use?
How many lights would each panel have if it were a Base 5 machine?

Study the notation on the machine very carefully. Can you write down the number shown on the machine? It is 264, 531, 792. Notice that we mark off the sets of 3 numbers with a comma which coincides with the sets of three panels. We always start by marking off sets of 3 from the right (the ones place).

Why do you think this method of using commas is particularly useful?

Notice that we count the millions, also the thousands, in hundreds, tens and ones.

Set these numbers on the machine, then write them down marking off in sets of 3 with the use of commas:

One hundred and ten million, one hundred and ten thousand.

Eleven million, eleven thousand and eleven.

One hundred million.

Five hundred and fifty-two million, three hundred and sixty-one thousand, nine hundred and ten.

Numbers on the machine can be written as, for example,

$$236,946,157$$

In words this would be:
Two hundred and thirty-six million, nine hundred and forty-six thousand, one hundred and fifty-seven.

We could write a kind of shorthand for this:

236 Million ⟶ 236 M

946 Thousand ⟶ 946 Th

157 Ones ⟶ 1H + 5T + 7U

If the machine showed the following number:
152,054,321

How would you read it?

What number is 1 less than 1000?

What number is 1 less than 1,000,000?

How many thousands make up a million?

How many ten thousands make up a million?

Which number do you think is the greater: a thousand hundred or a hundred thousand?

Make a counting board (or you could put 2 or more abaci together) to show large numbers, e.g.

millions			thousands			100	10	1
100	10	1	100	10	1			
○	○○○○○	○○○	○○	○○○○○○	○○	○○○○○○○○○	○○○○	

Write down the number displayed on the counting board above.

On your counting board, display some numbers of your own with counters, then write them down. Leave some columns blank in some of your numbers.

The population of the British Isles a few years ago was 52,175,625. We do not usually require a number to be so accurate and often give it as 'close' as we require. We could say that this population figure is:

50,000,000 to the nearest ten million
52,000,000 to the nearest million
52,200,000 to the nearest hundred thousand
52,180,000 to the nearest ten thousand
52,176,000 to the nearest thousand
52,175,600 to the nearest hundred
52,175,630 to the nearest ten
52,175,625

The top speed reached by one of the first space capsules was in the region of 17,545 miles per hour.

Give this speed rounded to:
a **the nearest 10**
b **the nearest 100**
c **the nearest 1000**

Think of some numbers of your own and see if you can round them off to the nearest million, 100 thousand, 10 thousand, thousand, and hundred.

It is a matter of convention that 25 expressed 'to the nearest ten' is taken as 30 rather than 20.

Populations

In the year between mid-1963 and mid-1964 the population of the world, as estimated by the United Nations Organisation, increased from 3160 million to 3215 million. The following three cities hold the largest populations:

New York City   11,291,000
Tokyo   10,248,000
London   8,186,830

Round off the above three population figures to:
a **the nearest million**
b **the nearest thousand**

Discuss with your teacher, or your partner, why it is very, very difficult to say what is the exact population figure for either the whole world or even a big city.

If the distance of the Earth from the Sun is given as 92,900,000 miles, as an approximate figure, what would this be 'rounded off' to the nearest million?

'Round off', or approximate, the following numbers to the nearest million:
300,756,231
  1,005,630
 20,798,897
158,123,123
799,999,999

Write the following without using words:
 5 million
 5 million 8 hundred thousand
1½ million
10 million 981 thousand 5 hundred and 3

The following is a list of the populations of the ten most populated countries in the world for 1964-5:

Brazil   76M
U.K.   54M
Indonesia   100M
U.S.A.   189M
India   460M
China   650M
U.S.S.R.   225M
W. Germany   55M
Pakistan   99M
Japan   96M

Sort these into an order which will give the country with the highest population first, the next highest, and so on. (Order of magnitude.)

When you have done this, make a block chart to show this information.

At the same time as the above information was available, Australia's population was given as 11,250,708, Canada's as 19,440,000 and New Zealand's as 2,627,483. Round these numbers off to the nearest million and include them in your graph.

From the graph, compare the sizes of the populations and then write some of them as inequalities, e.g.
Canada   19,440,000
Australia   11,250,708
$19,440,000 > 11,250,708$

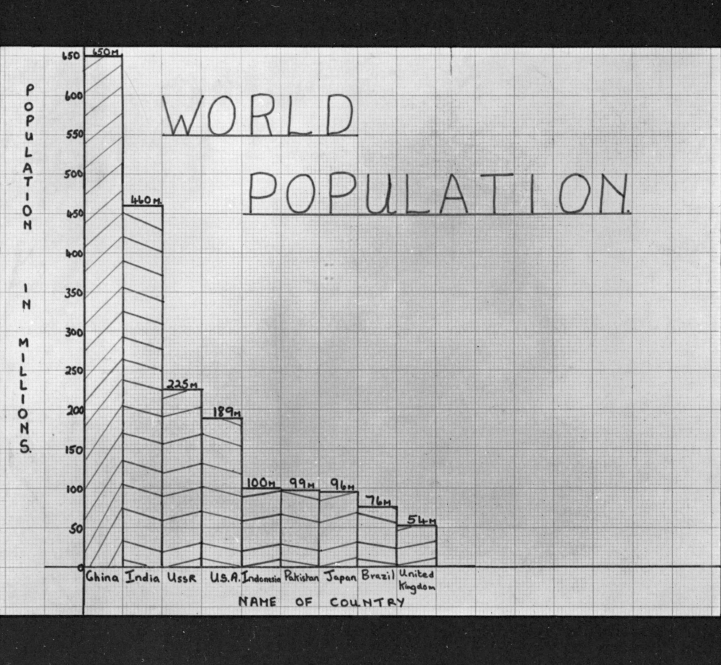

Expressing: 5,000.

5,000.

5 thousand.

$5 \times 1,000$.

50×100.

500×10.

5 th

Expressing: 7,500.

7,500.

7.5 thousand

7 thousand 5 hundred.

15×500.

150×50.

$1,500 \times 5$.

Expressing: 1,000.

1,000

1 th.

1 thousand

2×500.

20×50.

10×100

To give children an idea of why 'rounding off' large numbers is both sensible and meaningful, we can suggest 'Numbers in Space' as a topic of interest. The following will probably provide suitable material to introduce this:

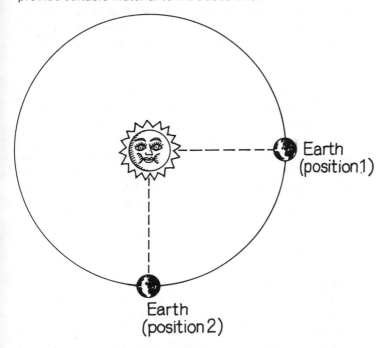

Earth (position 1)

Earth (position 2)

Earth is one of a family or set of 9 planets revolving or orbiting around the Sun. The nearest planet to the Sun is **Mercury**, then Venus, then Earth. The paths traced by these planets are not circular, but oval or elliptical.

Because the Sun is not in the centre of a circle, the distance between the Sun and each planet changes every second. So, we speak of distances between the Sun and the planets in terms of average or mean distances.

The average distance between the Earth and Sun is 92,912,000 miles. For Mercury it is 36,059,000 and for Venus 67,206,000 miles.

1 These distances have been rounded off to the nearest **million, thousand** or **hundred** miles. State which you think it is.
2 Round off these distances to the nearest million miles.

Here are some more average distances from the Sun to the other planets of the solar system:

Mars	**141,568,700 miles**
Uranus	**1,782,227,700 miles**
Neptune	**2,792,717,000 miles**
Jupiter	**483,401,300 miles**
Saturn	**886,270,100 miles**
Pluto	**3,671,660,400 miles**

A 'table' can be made in which the 9 planets of the solar system are listed to show their average distances from the Sun, in order. Begin with the planet nearest the Sun and give the distances to the nearest million miles.

Name of planet	Average distance from Sun (in millions of miles)
Mercury	36

The distance of the Moon from the Earth, at a particular time, is 238,857 miles. This could be written as:
238·857 thousand miles.

Here we have simply changed the unit of length from one mile to one thousand miles.

The Earth's diameter is 7913 miles. How could we write this in thousands of miles?

> The visible diameter of the Sun is 864,000 miles.
>
> Betelgeuse (Beetle-juice !) a super giant star, has a diameter about 450 times the diameter of the Sun. Which of these numbers do you think is the nearest to the measurement in miles of the diameter of Betelgeuse ?
>
>   1,500,000
>   400,000,000
>   800,000,000

Time

Large numbers are involved not only in the measurement of distance, but also in the measurement of time. We measure time in terms of the period which the Earth takes to orbit the Sun : we call it the year, and mark its passage by the recurrence of the seasons. Longer periods of time are marked by events in the life of a person, or of a nation or of the world itself. Time has relative significance : a day is long compared with a minute, but brief when compared with a decade. The child's appreciation of the scale of time grows gradually as he becomes older, but even the adult has difficulty in conceiving the length of time represented by a thousand years, or even by a couple of centuries.

One method of representing the 'distance of time' between events is to use a time-scale in the form of a line on which equal distances represent equal periods of time. The children may already have plotted their day's activities on such a time-scale, extending over 24 hours : if we attempt to construct a scale for a longer period of time, such as from the start of the twentieth century to the present day, then we need to reduce our scale to keep the line to a manageable length. If we allow 1 inch to a year, sixty years requires a line 5 feet long. On the same scale, the period since the Norman Conquest would need a line 75 feet long : a distance approximately equal to the perimeter of an average classroom. If the scale is reduced to ten years to the inch, a line extending as far back as the birth of Christ would be 17 feet long, and as we go further back in history and pre-history, the length of our line increases dramatically.

The division between primitive and civilised communities is marked by the invention of writing, which must have taken place by about 4000 B.C., when the civilisations of Sumeria, Babylon and Egypt began to flourish. Large neolithic communities are known to have existed in Greece and Turkey around 7000 B.C. to 6000 B.C.: our line, with 1 inch representing ten years, will need to be some 900 inches or about 75 feet long.

If we seek to show the whole history of mankind, we need to reduce our scale still further. Remains of **homo erectus**, a creature recognisable as man, have been dated as far back as 700,000 years ; at a thousand years to the inch, our line will be nearly 60 feet long, and on this scale the recorded history of man will occupy only the last 5 or 6 inches. The inhabitants of the caves at Lascaux, who recorded the passing scene in colour on the walls of the caves, lived some 15,000 years ago : the first members of our own species, **homo sapiens,** lived 50,000 years ago, although Neanderthal man was making tools 100,000 years ago.

The Age of Reptiles, which sooner or later captures the imagination of most children, occurred 150 million years ago. We need to represent the number 150,000,000 on our line : if we retain the scale of a thousand years to an inch, the line will be 150,000 inches, or about $2\frac{1}{2}$ miles long. If such a line is to be drawn in the classroom, it will be advisable to reduce the scale to an inch to a million years : the line will now be about 12 feet long. Man occupies a $\frac{1}{2}$ inch of this line : his recorded history will be represented by a mark at the end of the line of such a thickness as would be invisible to the unaided eye.

Life itself probably began on Earth three thousand million years ago – 3,000,000,000. The Earth itself is thought to have existed for about 4,500,000,000 years, whereas the universe is probably about 10,000,000,000 years old. A time-scale to show this period of time might be an inch to ten million years : the line would be some 80 feet long. The period in which life has existed on Earth would be represented by a length of some 25 feet ; the span of mankind's existence would be represented by a distance of about 0·07 inch.

Indices

Copy these sentences and complete them with the correct answer:

5 3 2 : The '3' means 3 × ☐
6 8 5 : The '6' means 6 × 100
3 1 5 , 0 8 0 : The '5' means 5 × ☐
3 1 5 , 0 8 0 : The '1' means 1 × 10,000
3 1 5 , 0 8 0 : The '3' means 3 × ☐
6 5 2 , 0 0 0 , 0 0 0 : The '2' means 2 × ☐
6 5 2 , 0 0 0 , 0 0 0 : The '5' means 5 × ☐
6 5 2 , 0 0 0 , 0 0 0 : The '6' means 6 × ☐

Can you fill in the missing numbers:
(4 × 100) + (3 × 10) + 6 = ☐
(5 × 1000) + (6 × 100) + (3 × 10) + 1 = ☐
(9 × 1000) + (2 × 100) + (0 × 10) + 6 = ☐

725 = (7 × ☐) + (2 × △) + ◯
1265 = (☐ × 1000) + (2 × △) + (◇ × 10) + 5
12,716 = (☐ × 1000) + (7 × △) + (◇ × 10) + ⬠

10×10=☐   10×10×10=☐
(10×10)×10=☐   10×(10×10)=☐
(10×10×10)×10=☐   (10×10×10) × (10×10×10) =☐

We can write 100 as 10 × 10 and 1000 as 10 × 10 × 10. Can you write 1,000,000 in similar form?

Complete the following 'table':
10   = 10
100   = 10 × 10
1000   = 10 × 10 × 10
10,000   =
100,000   =
1,000,000   =
10,000,000   =
100,000,000   =
1,000,000,000 =

Study your 'table' carefully. What do you notice?
Now have a look at this 'table':
10   = 10^1
100   = 10^2
1000   = 10^3
10,000   = 10^4
100,000   = 10^5
1,000,000 = 10^6

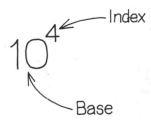

Can you carry on with this 'table'?

We call these little numerals, placed top right of the 10, **indices**. (Singular, index). Sometimes they are called **exponents**.

The two powers of 10 which you are probably most familiar with are:

10² **10 squared** **(10 × 10)**
10³ **10 cubed** **(10 × 10 × 10)**

What do you think 10^1 is?

To help you, take one of each of the different units of the Base 10 material in your Dienes apparatus and study it carefully.

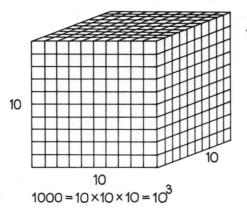

$1000 = 10 \times 10 \times 10 = 10^3$

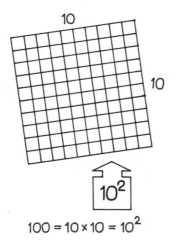

$100 = 10 \times 10 = 10^2$

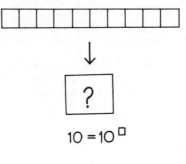

$10 = 10^{\square}$

$1 = 10^{\square}$

Can you make a guess as to how we can write this as a power of 10?

Make a list of the powers of 10 starting with 10^6 and then in the appropriate expanded notation, e.g.

10^6 = 10 × 10 × 10 × 10 × 10 × 10
10^5 =
10^4 =
10^3 =
10^2 =
10^1 =

$10^0 = 1$. This is a matter of definition, which fits in with later work, e.g.

$10^2 \times 10^3 = 10^5$ (add the indices, $2 + 3 = 5$)

and

$10^3 \times 10^0 = 10^3$ ($3 + 0 = 3$).

Some teachers may prefer from the start to proceed as follows:

$10^1 = 1 \times 10$

$10^2 = 1 \times 10 \times 10$

$10^3 = 1 \times 10 \times 10 \times 10$

etc.

10^2 is 1 multiplied by 10 twice.

10^1 is 1 multiplied by 10 once.

10^0 is 1 multiplied by 10 no .times, i.e. just 1.

You know that 3000 could be written as $3 \times 10 \times 10 \times 10$.

Write these numbers in the same way:

600 =	**5,000,000 =**
7000 =	**800,000 =**
17,000 =	**50,000 =**

Now write these numbers using indices, e.g.

$600 = 6 \times 10^2$

The number 3000 can be written in several ways:

3000

3 thousand

3×1000

$3 \times 10 \times 10 \times 10$

and

3×10^3

Write each of these numbers in five different ways:

93,000,000

250,000

What is 3×10^3? 7×10^5? 4×10^7?

5×10^2? 8×10^1? $(3 \times 10^2) + (6 \times 10)$?

So far we have dealt with expanded notation and indices in Base 10 only. We need not have started with Base 10, of course, and some teachers may even prefer to work in other bases, when introducing the index notation. The important thing is that we should now give a variety of bases and, ultimately, symbols as well as numerals, e.g.

x^3, a^2.

The Dienes M.A.B. material can be of use again here to introduce and consolidate previous work using indices.

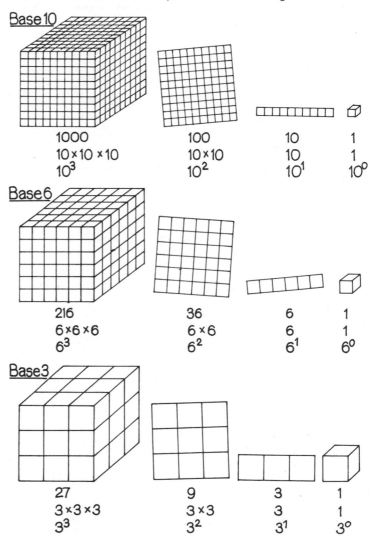

Base 10

1000	100	10	1
$10 \times 10 \times 10$	10×10	10	1
10^3	10^2	10^1	10^0

Base 6

216	36	6	1
$6 \times 6 \times 6$	6×6	6	1
6^3	6^2	6^1	6^0

Base 3

27	9	3	1
$3 \times 3 \times 3$	3×3	3	1
3^3	3^2	3^1	3^0

Can you complete the following table (the first example has been done for you):

symbol	expanded	number
6^3	$6 \times 6 \times 6$	216
	$3 \times 3 \times 3 \times 3$	81
4^2		16
2^5	$2 \times 2 \times 2 \times 2 \times 2$	
5^4		
7^3		343

How else do you think you could write these:

a^2 $x \times x \times x$ n^3 $y \times y$

You probably remember experimenting with triangular and square numbers.

Make a list of:
a the triangular numbers, and
b the square numbers, between 1 and 25.

Now study the following carefully:

$1^2 =$ ① $=$①
$2^2 =$ ① $+$ ③ $=$①$+$ ⟨1 + 2⟩
$3^2 =$ ③ $+$ ⑥ $=$ ⟨1 + 2⟩ $+$ ⟨1 + 2 + 3⟩
$4^2 =$ ⑥ $+$ ⑩ $=$ ⟨1 + 2 + 3⟩ $+$ ⟨1 + 2 + 3 + 4⟩
$5^2 =$ ⑩$+$ ⑮ $=$ ⟨1 + 2 + 3 + 4⟩ $+$ ⟨1 + 2 + 3 + 4 + 5⟩

First of all check the equalities.

What is the sum of two consecutive triangular numbers?

Could you continue the sequence with 6^2?

Write down the set of odd numbers between 1 and 10. Now see if you can complete the following. The first has been done as an example to help you:

$1 + 3$ $= 4$ $= 2^2$
$1 + 3 + 5$ $= \square$ $= 3^2$
$1 + 3 + 5 + 7$ $= 16$ $= \square$
$1 + 3 + 5 + 7 + \square = 25$ $= \square$

Can you continue these patterns?

We have seen some interesting patterns emerge from the set of odd numbers. Now let us see if there are any interesting progressions with the even numbers. Study the following and see if you can complete it:

2	= 2	$= 2^2 - 2$
2 + 4	= 6	$= 3^2 - 3$
2 + 4 + 6	= 12	$= 4^2 - 4$
2 + 4 + 6 + □	= 20	$= 5^2 - 5$
2 + 4 + 6 + 8 + 10	= □	$= 6^2 - □$

Can you continue with this?

How would you describe in words what is happening in each progression? Discuss this with your teacher.

Now have a look at this next progression and study it carefully:

2	= 2	$= 1^2 + 1$
2 + 4	= 6	$= 2^2 + 2$
2 + 4 + 6	= 12	$= 3^2 + 3$

See if you can continue this and then describe what is happening.

For teachers only

The formula for the first of the above is:
$(n + 1)^2 - (n + 1) = (2 \times 1) + (2 \times 2) + (2 \times 3) + \ldots + (2 \times n)$
and for the second:
$n^2 + n = (2 \times 1) + (2 \times 2) + (2 \times 3) + \ldots + (2 \times n)$
i.e. $\frac{1}{2}n(n + 1) = 1 + 2 + 3 + \ldots + n$.

How squares and cubes 'grow'
Write down a list of the squares and the cubes of the whole numbers from 1 to 10.

$1^2 = 1$	$1^3 = 1$
$2^2 = 4$	$2^3 = 8$
$3^2 =$	$3^3 =$
$4^2 =$	$4^3 =$
. . .	. . .

Now make a graph and plot these numbers to show how they 'grow'. Use different-coloured pencils or felt pens to show the comparison on the same graph.

Children enjoy words such as billion, trillion, quadrillion even if they all simply mean 'lots' to them. In fact, the word 'billion' in the United Kingdom means a million million, but in the United States it means a thousand million. It is, therefore, safer to use numerals. A million million takes some writing
1,000,000,000,000
and this is easier to see as 10^{12}.

Trillion 10^{18} (a million million million)
   (again, in the U.S. a 'trillion' is 10^{12})
Quadrillion 10^{24} (U.S. 10^{15})
Quintillion 10^{30}
Sextillion 10^{36}

10^{100} has been christened a googol. Children can appreciate that there is no 'highest' number.

Once indices have been introduced, they can be used in connection with the earlier work in this Chapter, e.g.

'The sea contains over 3×10^8 cubic miles of water.'

'The distance from the Earth to the Sun is approximately 93×10^6 miles.'

Appendix

If we use letters for numbers, it is easy to show that in arithmetic to any modulus the result of subtracting one number from a second is always the same as adding to the second the additive inverse of the first. Firstly, every number in arithmetic mod n does have an additive inverse: the inverse of 0 is 0, of 1 is (n-1), of 2 is (n-2), etc. Then, if □ is the result of subtracting b from a (i.e. □ = a − b), we know

a = □ + b

from the very definition of subtraction.

If now b* is the additive inverse of b, and we add this to both a and □ + b, we obtain

a + b* = □ + b + b* = □ + 0 = □

(using the fact that addition is associative) i.e.

a − b = a + (additive inverse of b).

The following publications of the Nuffield Mathematics Project appeared in 1967–8:

Introductory Guide

I do, and I understand ●■▼ (1967)

This Guide explains the intentions of the Project, gives detailed descriptions of the ways in which a changeover from conventional teaching can be made and faces many of the problems that will be met.

Teachers' Guides

Pictorial Representation 🔲 (1967)

Designed to help teachers of children between the ages of 5 and 10, this Guide deals with graphical representation in its many aspects.

Beginnings ▼ (1967)

This Guide deals with the early awareness of both the meaning of number and the relationships which can emerge from everyday experiences of measuring length, capacity, area, time, etc.

Mathematics Begins ❶ (1967)

A parallel Guide to *Beginnings* ▼ but more concerned with 'counting numbers' than with measurement. It contains a considerable amount of background information for the teacher.

Shape and Size ▼ (1967)

The first Guide concerned principally with geometrical ideas. It shows how geometrical concepts can be developed from the play stage in *Beginnings* ▼ to a clearer idea of what volume, area, horizontal and symmetrical really mean.

Computation and Structure ❷ (1967)

Here the concept of number is further developed. A section on the history of natural numbers and weights and measures leads on to the operation of addition, place value, different number bases, odd and even numbers, the application of number strips and number squares.

Shape and Size ▼ (1968)

Continues the geometrical work of ▼. Examination of two-dimensional shapes leads on to angles, symmetry and patterns, and links up with the more arithmetical work of ❷.

Computation and Structure ❸ (1968)

Suggests an abundance of ways of introducing children to multiplication so that they will understand what they are doing rather than simply follow rules.

Weaving Guides

Desk Calculators ◯▢▽ (1967)

Points out a number of ways in which calculators can be used constructively in teaching children number patterns, place value and multiplication and division in terms of repeated addition and subtraction.

How to Build a Pond ◯▢▽ (1967)

A facsimile reproduction of a class project.

The Teachers' Guides, together with *Graphs Leading to Algebra* ❷ (1969 : see opposite) and *Desk Calculators,* are summarised in *The Story So Far.*

Nuffield Mathematics Project publications appearing May, 1969:

Teachers' Guides

Graphs Leading to Algebra **2**
This Teachers' Guide develops the use of coordinates and introduces open sentences and truth sets. It goes on to deal with the graphical aspect of these mathematical statements, introducing graphs of inequalities, intersection of two graphs and graphs using integers.

Computation and Structure **4**
The main concern of this Teachers' Guide is with the introduction of the integers $\{ \ldots {}^{-}3, {}^{-}2, {}^{-}1, 0, {}^{+}1, {}^{+}2, {}^{+}3 \ldots \}$. In the past, children have been introduced to positive and negative numbers through the application of these and have been taught 'tricks' for using them in mathematical operations. This Guide builds up the idea of the integers in terms of ordered pairs of numbers before introducing the number line and other applications : this lays a sound foundation for operations on integers. The Guide ends with a short section on large numbers and indices.

Weaving Guides

Environmental Geometry ○□▽
One of the 'Weaving Guides', this book concentrates on making children more critically aware of shapes in their environment and the interrelationships of them. It deals with relative size and position and with recurring shapes and their properties. It is intended mainly for Infants and lower Juniors.

Probability and Statistics ○□▽
A 'Weaving Guide' designed to build up, in a very practical way, a critical approach to statistical information and assertions of probability. It demonstrates the many ways in which data can be collected and organised and it attempts to define the criteria for selecting the 'best' way for any given situation. Probability is introduced largely through games, but ways of predicting probable outcomes are investigated in detail.

Other publications

Problems – Green Set ○□▽
This publication consists of a Teachers' Book accompanied by a set of fifty-two cards for distribution to the children. Two further sets of Problems are in preparation.

The first set of Problems is intended for use with young Secondary pupils. The problems on the cards are reprinted in the Teachers' Book, with solutions and a considerable amount of background material and suggestions for follow-up work. All the topics covered by these cards are included in the Teachers' Guides already published, but they are presented in such a way that children who have not followed a 'Nuffield-type' course can do the problems and enjoy them.

The Story So Far ○□▽
This booklet is an outline of, and index to, the ground covered by the first nine Teachers' Guides of the Project. Its purpose is twofold : to provide easy references to topics in these Guides for those using them day by day (making a straight index proved an impossible task) ; and to save teachers of older children having to read through all the early Guides to find out 'what had happened previously'.

Consultative committee

Chairman   Professor W H Cockcroft
J W G Boucher
R C Lyness
Miss B M Mogford (1964–1966)
H S Mullaly (from 1966)
R Openshaw
N Payne (from 1967)
D R F Roseveare
J Shanks (from 1966)
A G Sillitto (died 1966)
P F Surman
Dr D R Taunt
Mrs D E Whittaker (from 1967)
F Woolaghan
Professor J Wrigley

Organiser
Dr Geoffrey Matthews

Team members

1965 – 1966   J W G Boucher
G B Corston
H Fletcher
Miss B A Jackson
D E Mansfield
Miss B M Mogford

1966 – 1967   D R Brighton
Miss I Campbell
H Fletcher
D E Mansfield
J H D Parker
Miss R K Tobias
A G Vosper

1967 – 1968   E A Albany
D R Brighton
Miss I Campbell
Miss R K Tobias
A G Vosper

1968 – 1969   E A Albany
D R Brighton
A G Vosper

Designers
Dodd & Dodd